Blairsville Junior High School
Blairsville, Pennsylvania

A POETRY SAMPLER

A POETRY SAMPLER

EDITED BY *Donald Hall*

FRANKLIN WATTS, INC.

575 Lexington Avenue · New York 22

FOR TED AND JAY LEWIS

SECOND PRINTING
Library of Congress Catalog Card Number: 61–10063
Copyright © 1962 by Donald Hall
Printed in the United States of America

ACKNOWLEDGMENTS

The editor and publisher have made every effort to trace the ownership of all material contained herein. It is their belief that the necessary permissions from publishers, authors, and authorized agents have been obtained in all cases. In the event of any question arising as to the use of any material, the editor and publisher, while expressing regret for any error unconsciously made, will be pleased to make the necessary correction in future editions of this book.

Appleton-Century-Crofts, Inc.
for Vachel Lindsay, "The Flower-Fed Buffaloes" from *Going-to-the-Stars*, Copyright 1926 by D. Appleton & Company. Reprinted by permission of the publishers Appleton-Century-Crofts, an affiliate of Meredith Press.

The Clarendon Press, Oxford
for Robert Bridges, "London Snow." Reprinted by permission of the publisher.

J. M. Dent & Sons Ltd.
for Dylan Thomas, "Do not go Gentle into that Good Night," and "In My Craft or Sullen Art." Reprinted by permission of the publisher.

Doubleday & Company, Inc.
for Theodore Roethke, "Dolor" from *The Lost Son and Other Poems*, Copyright 1947 by Theodore Roethke. Reprinted by permission of Doubleday & Company, Inc.
for Rudyard Kipling, "The Way Through the Woods," from *Rewards and Fairies*, Copyright 1910 by Rudyard Kipling. Reprinted by permission of Mrs. George Bambridge and Doubleday & Company, Inc.

Faber and Faber Ltd.
for T. S. Eliot, "Journey of the Magi," "Aunt Helen," "Cousin Nancy," "The Hippopotamus," "Landscapes I," and "Landscapes II," from *Collected Poems*, reprinted by permission of the publishers.
for Louis MacNeice, "Bagpipe Music," from *85 Poems*, reprinted by permission of the publishers.
for Edwin Muir, "The Horses." Reprinted by permission of the publishers.

Grove Press, Inc.
for Edwin Muir, "The Horses" from *One Foot in Eden*, published 1957 by Grove Press. Reprinted by permission of the publisher.

Harcourt, Brace and Company, Inc.
for T. S. Eliot, "Journey of the Magi," "Aunt Helen," "Cousin Nancy," "The Hippopotamus," and "Landscapes: 'New Hampshire' and 'Virginia'," from *Collected Poems 1909-1935*, by T. S. Eliot, Copyright 1936 by Harcourt, Brace and World, Inc. and reprinted with their permission.
for Richard Wilbur, "Tywater" from *The Beautiful Changes*, Copyright 1947 by Richard Wilbur. Reprinted by permission of Harcourt, Brace and World, Inc.

[iv]

[v]

Jonathan Cape and Harrison Smith, Inc. 1957 by Frieda Ravagli. Reprinted by permission of The Viking Press, Inc.

A. P. Watt & Son
 for Robert Graves, "To Juan at the Winter Solstice" and "The Legs" from *Collected Poems 1955*, published by Doubleday & Co., Inc. and Cassell & Co. Ltd. © 1955. Reprinted by permission of Co-Productions Roturman S.A.

Wesleyan University Press
 for Louis Simpson, "A Dream of Governors" from *A Dream of Governors*, © 1957 by Louis Simpson. Reprinted by permission of Wesleyan University Press.
 for Barbara Howes, "Cat on Couch" from *Light and Dark*, © 1955 by Barbara Howes. Reprinted by permission of Wesleyan University Press.
 for Vassar Miller, "Autumnal Spring Song" from *Wage War on Silence*, Copyright © 1960 by Vassar Miller. Reprinted by permission of Wesleyan University Press.
 for Robert Francis, "Farm Boy After Summer" and "Hide and Seek" from *The Orb Weaver*, Copyright 1959 and 1946 by Robert Francis. Reprinted by permission of Wesleyan University Press.

THE PURPOSE OF THIS BOOK

A Poetry Sampler is an introduction to English poetry by way of its best poets.

If you want to appreciate an art, study the best examples of it. Some people assume that the third- and second-rate are rungs on a ladder which leads to the first-rate, but, on the contrary, inferior art only blocks the passage to good art. Beginning with the best, you will learn to discriminate between the genuine work of art and the slick imitation. And there is no way to acquire this judgment except by exposure to the best.

The poems in *A Poetry Sampler* are some of the best in our language. The poets are either the great names of the past or the foremost of the young poets, who will have special meaning for contemporary readers.

These poems are selected from the long rows of Collected Works, especially for the reader who is new to poetry. Poems omitted are those that are difficult because of their topical allusions or archaic language. The reader can move to more difficult poems on the next stage of his progress, when his introduction to poetry is complete.

Our poetry is something which all of us own with our language, but few people realize the greatness of the art which is open to them. If our civilization should disappear, and a thousand years go by, our English-speaking countries might well be remembered for the sake of a volume no larger than this one. The poetry of the English language, like Greek drama, is one of the greatest literatures of the world.

This book is an introduction not only to greatness but to great pleasures. Poems are pleasures to the mind and to the emotions. Also, poems go deeply into the darkness of our selves and are pleasures to the imagination. To read a poem we must hear it with the physical ear, and we must follow its plot or argument with the mind. But we must also enter the experience of the whole poem, and live inside it. The way to learn to read poems for this intimate joy is to read them and reread them.

May you enjoy *A Poetry Sampler*!

—DONALD HALL

CONTENTS

[xii]

[xxiii]

EDWARD, EDWARD

Anonymous

ફ⊷ ⊷ફ

"Why does your brand so drop with blood,
    Edward, Edward?
Why does your brand so drop with blood?
    And why so sad go ye, O?"
"O I have killed my hawk so good,
    Mother, mother;
O I have killed my hawk so good,
    And I had no more but he, O."

"Your hawk's blood was never so red,
    Edward, Edward;
Your hawk's blood was never so red,
    My dear son, I tell thee, O."
"O I have killed my red-roan steed,
    Mother, mother;
O I have killed my red-roan steed,
    That erst was so fair and free, O."

"Your steed was old, and ye have got more,
    Edward, Edward;
Your steed was old and ye have got more;
    Some other dule ye dree, O."
"O I have killed my father dear,
    Mother, mother;
O I have killed my father dear,
    Alas, and woe is me, O!"

"And whatten penance will ye dree for that?
    Edward, Edward?
And whatten penance will ye dree for that?
    My dear son, now tell me, O."
"I'll set my feet in yonder boat,
    Mother, mother;

brand: sword   *erst:* formerly   *dule ye dree:* sorrow you bear

[1]

I'll set my feet in yonder boat,
    And I'll fare over the sea, O."

"And what will ye do with your towers and your hall,
    Edward, Edward?
And what will ye do with your towers and your hall,
    That were so fair to see, O?"
"I'll let them stand till they down fall,
    Mother, mother;
I'll let them stand till they down fall,
    For here never more must I be, O."

"And what will ye leave to your bairns and your wife,
    Edward, Edward?
And what will ye leave to your bairns and your wife,
    When ye go over the sea, O?"
"The world's room: let them beg through life,
    Mother, mother;
The world's room: let them beg through life;
    For them never more will I see, O."

"And what will ye leave to your own mother dear,
    Edward, Edward?
And what will ye leave to your own mother dear,
    My dear son, now tell me, O?"
"The curse of hell from me shall ye bear,
    Mother, mother;
The curse of hell from me shall ye bear:
    Such counsels ye gave to me, O!"

¶ "Edward, Edward," and "Sir Patrick Spens," which follows, are old Scots ballads, composed by unknown authors
and available in various versions.

---

bairns: children

SIR PATRICK SPENS

Anonymous

ᘒ❧ ❧ᘓ

The king sits in Dunfermlin town
 Drinking the blood-red wine;
"O where will I get a skilful skipper
 To sail this new ship of mine?"

O up and spoke an eldern knight,
 Sat at the king's right knee;
"Sir Patrick Spens is the best sailor
 That ever sailed the sea."

The king has written a long letter,
 And sealed it with his hand,
And sent it to Sir Patrick Spens,
 Was walking on the strand.

"To Noroway, to Noroway,
 To Noroway o'er the foam;
The king's daughter o' Noroway,
 'Tis thou must bring her home."

The first line that Sir Patrick read
 A loud laugh laughed he;
The next line that Sir Patrick read
 The tear blinded his eye.

"O who is this has done this deed
 And told the king o' me,
To send us out, at this time of the year,
 To sail upon the sea?

"Be it wind, be it wet, be it hail, be it sleet,
 Our ship must sail the foam;

eldern: olden

[3]

The king's daughter o' Noroway,
    'Tis we must fetch her home."

They hoisted their sails on Monenday morn
    With all the speed they may;
And they have landed in Noroway
    Upon a Wodensday.

They hadna been a week, a week,
    In Noroway, but two,
When that the lords o' Noroway
    Began aloud to say,

"Ye Scottishmen spend all our king's gold,
    And a' our queen's fee!"
"Ye lie, ye lie, ye liars loud!
    For loud I hear ye lie!

"For I brought as much white money,
    As gane my men and me,
And I brought a half-fou o' good red gold,
    Out o'er the sea with me.

"Make ready, make ready, my merry men all!
    Our good ship sails the morn."
"Now ever alack, my master dear,
    I fear a deadly storm.

"I saw the new moon late yestreen
    With the old moon in her arm;
And if we go to sea, master,
    I fear we'll come to harm."

They hadna sailed a league, a league,
    A league but barely three,
When the sky grew dark, and the wind blew loud,
    And gurly grew the sea.

gane: suffice   *half-fou:* half-bushel   *yestreen:* yesterday
gurly: stormy

[4]

The anchors broke, and the topmast sprang,
    It was such a deadly storm:
And the waves came over the broken ship
    Till all her sides were torn.

"Go fetch a web of the silken cloth,
    Another of the twine,
And bind them into our ship's side,
    And let not the sea come in."

They fetched a web of the silken cloth,
    Another of the twine,
And they bound them round that good ship's side,
    But still the sea came in.

O loath, loath were our good Scots lords
    To wet their cork-heeled shoon,
But long before all the play was play'd
    They wet their hats aboon.

And many was the feather bed
    That floated on the foam,
And many was the good lord's son
    That never more came home.

O long, long, may the ladies sit,
    With their fans in their hand,
Before they see Sir Patrick Spens
    Come sailing to the strand!

And long, long may the maidens sit
    With their gold combs in their hair,
A-waiting for their own dear loves!
    For them they'll see no more.

O forty miles off Aberdeen,
    'Tis fifty fathoms deep;

shoon: shoes   *aboon:* above

[5]

And there lies good Sir Patrick Spens,
      With the Scots lord at his feet.

¶ Later authors sometimes imitated the popular ballad.
See if you can notice the difference.

LA BELLE DAME SANS MERCI

John Keats (1795–1821)

ह~ ~ई

"O what can ail thee, knight-at-arms,
      Alone and palely loitering?
The sedge has wither'd from the lake,
      And no birds sing.

"O what can ail thee, knight-at-arms,
      So haggard and so woe-begone?
The squirrel's granary is full,
      And the harvest's done.

"I see a lily on thy brow
      With anguish moist and fever-dew,
And on thy cheeks a fading rose
      Fast withereth too."

"I met a lady in the meads,
      Full beautiful—a faery's child,
Her hair was long, her foot was light,
      And her eyes were wild.

[6]

"I made a garland for her head,
	And bracelets too, and fragrant zone;
She look'd at me as she did love,
	And made sweet moan.

"I set her on my pacing steed
	And nothing else saw all day long,
For sidelong would she bend, and sing
	A faery's song.

"She found me roots of relish sweet,
	And honey wild and manna-dew,
And sure in language strange she said
	'I love thee true.'

"She took me to her elfin grot,
	And there she wept, and sigh'd full sore,
And there I shut her wild wild eyes
	With kisses four.

"And there she lullèd me asleep,
	And there I dream'd—Ah! woe betide!
The latest dream I ever dream'd
	On the cold hill's side.

"I saw pale kings and princes too,
	Pale warriors, death-pale were they all;
They cried—'La belle Dame sans Merci
	Hath thee in thrall!'

"I saw their starved lips in the gloam
	With horrid warning gaped wide,
And I awoke and found me here,
	On the cold hill's side.

"And this is why I sojourn here
	Alone and palely loitering,

zone: a belt
grot: grotto

[7]

Though the sedge is wither'd from the lake
And no birds sing."

¶ The next poem is the work of a modern American poet,
but imitates even the language of the old poems.

BALLAD OF THE GOODLY FERE

Ezra Pound (1885–)

ॐ

Simon Zelotes speaketh it somewhile after the Crucifixion

Ha' we lost the goodliest fere o' all
For the priests and the gallows tree?
Aye lover he was of brawny men,
O' ships and the open sea.

When they came wi' a host to take Our Man
His smile was good to see,
"First let these go!" quo' our Goodly Fere,
"Or I'll see ye damned," says he.

Aye he sent us out through the crossed high spears
And the scorn of his laugh rang free,
"Why took ye not me when I walked about
Alone in the town?" says he.

Oh we drunk his "Hale" in the good red wine
When we last made company,
No capon priest was the Goodly Fere
But a man o' men was he.

fere: companion

[8]

I ha' seen him drive a hundred men
Wi' a bundle o' cords swung free,
That they took the high and holy house
For their pawn and treasury.

They'll no' get him a' in a book I think
Though they write it cunningly;
No mouse of the scrolls was the Goodly Fere
But aye loved the open sea.

If they think they ha' snared our Goodly Fere
They are fools to the last degree.
"I'll go to the feast," quo' our Goodly Fere,
"Though I go to the gallows tree.

"Ye ha' seen me heal the lame and blind,
And wake the dead," says he,
"Ye shall see one thing to master all:
'Tis how a brave man dies on the tree."

A son of God was the Goodly Fere
That bade us his brothers be.
I ha' seen him cow a thousand men.
I ha' seen him upon the tree.

He cried no cry when they drave the nails
And the blood gushed hot and free,
The hounds of the crimson sky gave tongue
But never a cry cried he.

I ha' seen him cow a thousand men
On the hills o' Galilee,
They whined as he walked out calm between,
Wi' his eyes like the gray o' the sea,

Like the sea that brooks no voyaging
With the winds unleashed and free,
Like the sea that he cowed at Genseret
Wi' twey words spoke' suddenly.

[9]

A master of men was the Goodly Fere,
A mate of the wind and sea,
If they think they ha' slain our Goodly Fere
They are fools eternally.

I ha' seen him eat o' the honey-comb
Sin' they nailed him to the tree.

¶ The next poem is by a new English poet, writing about cowboys. He plays with the old forms of the ballad, and when he has his cowboys drink tea, he is not being naive; he is imitating the kind of mistakes the old writers made.

COWBOY SONG

Charles Causley (1917–)

I come from Salem County
    Where the silver melons grow,
Where the wheat is as sweet as an angel's feet
    And the zithering zephyrs blow.
I walk the blue bone-orchard
    In the apple-blossom snow,
When the teasy bees take their honeyed ease
    And the marmalade moon hangs low.

My Maw sleeps prone on the prairie
    In a boulder eiderdown,
Where the pickled stars in their little jam-jars
    Hang in a hoop to town.
I haven't seen Paw since a Sunday
    In eighteen seventy-three

When he packed his snap in a bitty mess-trap
    And said he'd be home by tea.

Fled is my fancy sister
    All weeping like the willow,
And dead is the brother I loved like no other
    Who once did share my pillow.
I fly the florid water
    Where run the seven geese round
O the townsfolk talk to see me walk
    Six inches off the ground.

Across the map of midnight
    I trawl the turning sky,
In my green glass the salt fleets pass
    The moon her fire-float by.
The girls go gay in the valley
    When the boys come down from the farm,
Don't run, my joy, from a poor cowboy,
    I won't do you no harm.

The bread of my twentieth birthday
    I buttered with the sun,
Though I sharpen my eyes with lovers' lies
    I'll never see twenty-one.
Light is my shirt with lilies,
    And lined with lead my hood,
On my face as I pass is a plate of brass,
    And my suit is made of wood.

"IS MY TEAM PLOUGHING"

A. E. Housman (1859–1936)

"Is my team ploughing,
  That I used to drive
And hear the harness jingle
  When I was man alive?"

Ay, the horses trample,
  The harness jingles now;
No change though you lie under
  The land you used to plough.

"Is football playing
  Along the river shore,
With lads to chase the leather,
  Now I stand up no more?"

Ay, the ball is flying,
  The lads play heart and soul;
The goal stands up, the keeper
  Stands up to keep the goal.

"Is my girl happy,
  That I thought hard to leave,
And has she tired of weeping
  As she lies down at eve?"

Ay, she lies down lightly
  She lies not down to weep:
Your girl is well contented.
  Be still, my lad, and sleep.

"Is my friend hearty,
  Now I am thin and pine;

And has he found to sleep in
    A better bed than mine?"

Ay, lad, I lie easy,
    I lie as lads would choose;
I cheer a dead man's sweetheart.
    Never ask me whose.

¶ Many poems in the form of a story are not actually ballads. In a real ballad, the action is what matters. In the next poem, the poet has something in mind besides his tale.

THE BATTLE OF BLENHEIM

Robert Southey (*1774–1843*)

It was a summer evening,
    Old Kaspar's work was done,
And he before his cottage door
    Was sitting in the sun,
And by him sported on the green
His little grandchild Wilhelmine.

She saw her brother Peterkin
    Roll something large and round,
Which he beside the rivulet
    In playing there had found;
He came to ask what he had found
That was so large, and smooth, and round.

Old Kaspar took it from the boy,
    Who stood expectant by;

[13]

And then the old man shook his head,
 And, with a natural sigh,
" 'Tis some poor fellow's skull," said he,
"Who fell in the great victory.

"I find them in the garden,
 For there's many here about;
And often when I go to plough,
 The ploughshare turns them out:
For many thousand men," said he,
"Were slain in that great victory."

"Now tell us what 'twas all about,"
 Young Peterkin he cries;
And little Wilhelmine looks up
 With wonder-waiting eyes;
"Now tell us all about the war,
And what they fought each other for."

"It was the English," Kaspar cried,
 "Who put the French to rout;
But what they fought each other for,
 I could not well make out;
But everybody said," quoth he,
"That 'twas a famous victory.

"My father lived at Blenheim then,
 Yon little stream hard by;
They burnt his dwelling to the ground,
 And he was forced to fly;
So with his wife and child he fled,
Nor had he where to rest his head.

"With fire and sword the country round
 Was wasted far and wide,
And many a childing mother then
 And newborn baby died;
But things like that, you know, must be
At every famous victory.

[14]

"They say it was a shocking sight
    After the field was won;
For many thousand bodies here
    Lay rotting in the sun;
But things like that, you know, must be
After a famous victory.

"Great praise the Duke of Marlbro' won,
    And our good Prince Eugene."
"Why, 'twas a very wicked thing!"
    Said little Wilhelmine,
"Nay . . . nay . . . my little girl," quoth he,
"It was a famous victory.

"And everybody praised the Duke
    Who this great fight did win."
"But what good came of it at last?"
    Quoth little Peterkin.
"Why that I cannot tell," said he,
"But 'twas a famous victory."

¶ The inspiration for Coleridge's "Rime of the Ancient Mariner" comes from the old ballads, too, and it is the most ambitious poem ever modeled on them.

THE RIME OF THE ANCIENT MARINER

Samuel Taylor Coleridge (1772–1834)

ﻬ ﻬ

ARGUMENT

How a ship having passed the Line was driven by storms to the cold Country toward the South Pole; and how from thence she made her course to the tropical Latitude of the Great Pacific

Ocean; and of the strange things that befel; and in what manner
the Ancient Mariner came back to his own Country.

PART I

It is an ancient Mariner,
And he stoppeth one of three.
"By thy long gray beard and glittering eye,
Now wherefore stopp'st thou me?

The Bridegroom's doors are opened wide,
And I am next of kin;
The guests are met, the feast is set:
May'st hear the merry din."

He holds him with his skinny hand,
"There was a ship," quoth he.
"Hold off! unhand me, gray-beard loon!"
Eftsoons his hand dropt he.

He holds him with his glittering eye—
The Wedding-Guest stood still,
And listens like a three years' child:
The Mariner hath his will.

The Wedding-Guest sat on a stone:
He cannot choose but hear;
And thus spake on that ancient man,
The bright-eyed Mariner.

"The ship was cheered, the harbor cleared,
Merrily did we drop
Below the kirk, below the hill,
Below the lighthouse top.

The Sun came up upon the left,
Out of the sea came he!
And he shone bright, and on the right
Went down into the sea.

Higher and higher every day,
Till over the mast at noon—"
The Wedding-Guest here beat his breast,
For he heard the loud bassoon.

The bride hath paced into the hall,
Red as a rose is she;
Nodding their heads before her goes
The merry minstrelsy.

The Wedding-Guest he beat his breast,
Yet he cannot choose but hear;
And thus spake on that ancient man,
The bright-eyed Mariner.

"And now the Storm-blast came, and he
Was tyrannous and strong:
He struck with his o'ertaking wings,
And chased us south along.

With sloping masts and dipping prow,
As who pursued with yell and blow
Still treads the shadow of his foe,
And forward bends his head,
The ship drove fast, loud roared the blast,
And southward aye we fled.

And now there came both mist and snow,
And it grew wondrous cold:
And ice, mast-high, came floating by,
As green as emerald.

And through the drifts the snowy clifts
Did send a dismal sheen:
Nor shapes of men nor beasts we ken—
The ice was all between.

The ice was here, the ice was there,
The ice was all around:

[17]

It crack'd and growled, and roared and
    howled,
Like noises in a swound!

At length did cross an Albatross,
Through the fog it came;
As if it had been a Christian soul,
We hailed it in God's name.

It ate the food it ne'er had eat,
And round and round it flew.
The ice did split with a thunder-fit;
The helmsman steered us through!

And a good south wind sprung up behind;
The Albatross did follow,
And every day, for food or play,
Came to the mariners' hollo!

In mist or cloud, on mast or shroud,
It perched for vespers nine;
Whiles all the night, through fog-smoke
    white,
Glimmer'd the white Moonshine."

"God save thee, ancient Mariner!
From the fiends, that plague thee thus!—
Why look'st thou so?"—"With my cross-
    bow
I shot the Albatross."

Till a great sea-bird, called the Albatross, came through the snow-fog, and was received with great joy and hospitality.

And lo! the Albatross proveth a bird of good omen, and followeth the ship as it returned northward through fog and floating ice.

The ancient Mariner inhospitably killeth the pious bird of good omen.

PART II

"The Sun now rose upon the right:
Out of the sea came he,
Still hid in mist, and on the left,
Went down into the sea.

swound: swoon

[18]

And the good south wind still blew behind,
But no sweet bird did follow,
Nor any day for food or play
Came to the mariners' hollo!

And I had done a hellish thing,
And it would work 'em woe:
For all averred, I had kill'd the bird
That made the breeze to blow.
Ah wretch! said they, the bird to slay,
That made the breeze to blow!

His shipmates cry out against the ancient Mariner, for killing the bird of good luck.

Nor dim nor red, like God's own head,
The glorious Sun uprist:
Then all averred I had kill'd the bird
That brought the fog and mist.
'Twas right, said they, such birds to slay,
That bring the fog and mist.

But when the fog cleared off, they justify the same, and thus make themselves accomplices in the crime.

The fair breeze blew, the white foam flew,
The furrow followed free;
We were the first that ever burst
Into that silent sea.

The fair breeze continues; the ship enters the Pacific Ocean, and sails northward, even till it reaches the Line.

Down dropt the breeze, the sails dropt
        down,
'Twas sad as sad could be;
And we did speak only to break
The silence of the sea!

The ship hath been suddenly becalmed.

All in a hot and copper sky,
The bloody Sun, at noon,
Right up above the mast did stand,
No bigger than the Moon.

Day after day, day after day,
We stuck, nor breath nor motion;
As idle as a painted ship
Upon a painted ocean.

[19]

Water, water, everywhere,
And all the boards did shrink;
Water, water, everywhere,
Nor any drop to drink.

And the Albatross
begins to be avenged.

The very deep did rot: O Christ!
That ever this should be!
Yea, slimy things did crawl with legs
Upon the slimy sea.

About, about, in reel and rout
The death-fires danced at night;
The water, like a witch's oils,
Burnt green, and blue and white.

And some in dreams assurèd were
Of the Spirit that plagued us so;
Nine fathom deep he had followed us
From the land of mist and snow.

A Spirit had followed
them; one of the in-
visible inhabitants of
this planet, neither de-
parted souls nor angels;
concerning whom the
learned Jew, Josephus,
and the Platonic Con-
stantinopolitan, Michael
Psellus, may be con-
sulted. They are very
numerous, and there is
no climate or element
without one or more.

And every tongue, through utter drought,
Was withered at the root;
We could not speak, nor more than if
We had been choked with soot.

Ah! well-a-day! what evil looks
Had I from old and young!
Instead of the cross, the Albatross
About my neck was hung."

The shipmates in their
sore distress, would fain
throw the whole guilt on
the ancient Mariner: in
sign whereof they hang
the dead sea-bird round
his neck.

PART III

"There passed a weary time. Each throat
Was parched, and glazed each eye.
A weary time! a weary time!
How glazed each weary eye,
When looking westward, I beheld
A something in the sky.

The ancient Mariner
beholdeth a sign in the
element afar off.

[20]

At first it seemed a little speck,
And then it seemed a mist;
It moved and moved, and took at last
A certain shape, I wist.

A speck, a mist, a shape, I wist!
And still it neared and neared:
As if it dodged a water-sprite,
It plunged, and tacked, and veered.

With throats unslaked, with black lips
 baked,
We could nor laugh nor wail;
Through utter drought all dumb we stood!
I bit my arm, I sucked the blood,
And cried, A sail! a sail!

At its nearer approach, it seemeth him to be a ship; and at a dear ransom he freeth his speech from the bonds of thirst.

With throats unslaked, with black lips
 baked,
Agape they heard me call:
Gramercy! they for joy did grin,
And all at once their breath drew in,
As they were drinking all.

A flash of joy.

'See! see!' (I cried) 'she tacks no more!
Hither to work us weal;
Without a breeze, without a tide,
She steadies with upright keel!'

And horror follows. For can it be a ship that comes onward without wind or tide?

The western wave was all a-flame,
The day was well nigh done!
Almost upon the western wave
Rested the broad, bright Sun;
When that strange shape drove suddenly
Betwixt us and the Sun.

And straight the Sun was flecked with bars
(Heaven's Mother send us grace!)

It seemeth him but the skeleton of a ship.

wist: knew

[2 1]

As if through a dungeon-grate he peer'd
With broad and burning face.

Alas! (thought I, and my heart beat loud)
How fast she nears and nears!
Are those her sails that glance in the sun,
Like restless gossameres?

Are those her ribs through which the Sun
Did peer, as through a grate?
And is that Woman all her crew?
Is that a Death? and are there two?
Is Death that Woman's mate?

And its ribs are seen as bars on the face of the setting Sun. The Specter-Woman and her Death-mate, and no other, on board the skeleton ship.

Her lips were red, her looks were free,
Her locks were yellow as gold:
Her skin was as white as leprosy,
The Nightmare Life-in-Death was she,
Who thicks man's blood with cold.

Like vessel, like crew!

The naked hulk alongside came,
And the twain were casting dice;
'The game is done! I've won! I've won!'
Quoth she, and whistles thrice.

Death and Life-in-Death have diced for the ship's crew, and she (the latter) winneth the ancient Mariner. No twilight within the courts of the Sun.

The Sun's rim dips; the stars rush out:
At one stride comes the dark;
With far-heard whisper, o'er the sea,
Off shot the specter-bark.

We listened and looked sideways up!
Fear at my heart, as at a cup,
My life-blood seemed to sip!
The stars were dim, and thick the night,
The steersman's face by his lamp gleamed
        white;
From the sails the dew did drip—
Till clomb above the eastern bar

At the rising of the Moon,

The horned Moon, with one bright star
Within the nether tip.

One after one, by the star-dogged Moon,
Too quick for groan or sigh,
Each turned his face with a ghastly pang,
And cursed me with his eye.

One after another,

Four times fifty living men
(And I heard nor sigh nor groan)
With heavy thump, a lifeless lump,
They dropped down one by one.

His shipmates drop
down dead.

The souls did from their bodies fly,—
They fled to bliss or woe!
And every soul, it passed me by
Like the whizz of my cross-bow!"

But Life-in-Death
begins her work on
the ancient Mariner.

Part IV

"I fear thee, ancient Mariner!
I fear thy skinny hand!
And thou art long, and lank, and brown,
As is the ribbed sea-sand.

The Wedding-Guest
feareth that a Spirit is
talking to him;

I fear thee and thy glittering eye,
And thy skinny hand so brown."—
"Fear not, fear not, thou Wedding-Guest!
This body dropt not down.

But the ancient Mariner
assureth him of his
bodily life, and proceed-
eth to relate his horrible
penance.

Alone, alone, all, all alone,
Alone on a wide wide sea!
And never a saint took pity on
My soul in agony.

The many men, so beautiful!
And they all dead did lie:
And a thousand thousand slimy things
Lived on; and so did I.

He despiseth the
creatures of the calm,

[23]

I looked upon the rotting sea,
And drew my eyes away;
I looked upon the rotting deck,
And there the dead men lay.

I looked to heaven, and tried to pray;
But or ever a prayer had gusht,
A wicked whisper came, and made
My heart as dry as dust.

I closed my lids, and kept them close,
And the balls like pulses beat;
But the sky and the sea, and the sea and the
    sky
Lay like a load on my weary eye,
And the dead were at my feet.

The cold sweat melted from their limbs,
Nor rot nor reek did they:
The look with which they looked on me
Had never passed away.

An orphan's curse would drag to hell
A spirit from on high;
But oh! more horrible than that
Is the curse in a dead man's eye!
Seven days, seven nights, I saw that curse,
And yet I could not die.

The moving Moon went up the sky,
And nowhere did abide:
Softly she was going up,
And a star or two beside—

Her beams bemocked the sultry main,
Like April hoar-frost spread;
But where the ship's huge shadow lay,
The charmèd water burnt alway
A still and awful red.

[24]

Beyond the shadow of the ship,
I watched the water-snakes:
They moved in tracks of shining white,
And when they reared, the elfish light
Fell off in hoary flakes.

Within the shadow of the ship
I watched their rich attire:
Blue, glossy green, and velvet black,
They coiled and swam; and every track
Was a flash of golden fire.

O happy living things! no tongue
Their beauty might declare:
A spring of love gushed from my heart,
And I blessed them unaware:
Sure my kind saint took pity on me,
And I blessed them unaware.

The self-same moment I could pray;
And from my neck so free
The Albatross fell off, and sank
Like lead into the sea."

PART V

"O sleep! it is a gentle thing,
Beloved from pole to pole!
To Mary Queen the praise be given!
She sent the gentle sleep from Heaven,
That slid into my soul.

The silly buckets on the deck,
That had so long remained,
I dreamt that they were filled with dew;
And when I awoke, it rained.

My lips were wet, my throat was cold,
My garments all were dank;

The marginal glosses are:

- By the light of the Moon he beholdeth God's creatures of the great calm.
- Their beauty and their happiness.
- He blesseth them in his heart.
- The spell begins to break.
- By grace of the holy Mother, the ancient Mariner is refreshed with rain.

[25]

Sure I had drunken in my dreams,
And still my body drank.

I moved, and could not feel my limbs:
I was so light—almost
I thought that I had died in sleep,
And was a blessèd ghost.

And soon I heard a roaring wind:
It did not come anear;
But with its sound it shook the sails,
That were so thin and sere.

The upper air burst into life!
And a hundred fire-flags sheen,
To and fro they were hurried about!
And to and fro, and in and out,
The wan stars danced between.

And the coming wind did roar more loud,
And the sails did sigh like sedge;
And the rain poured down from one black
        cloud;
The Moon was at its edge.

The thick black cloud was cleft, and still
The Moon was at its side:
Like waters shot from some high crag,
The lightning fell with never a jag,
A river steep and wide.

The loud wind never reached the ship,
Yet now the ship moved on!
Beneath the lightning and the Moon
The dead men gave a groan.

They groaned, they stirred, they all uprose,
Nor spake, nor moved their eyes;
It had been strange, even in a dream,
To have seen those dead men rise.

He heareth sounds and
seeth strange sights and
commotions in the sky
and the elements.

The bodies of the ship's
crew are inspirited, and
the ship moves on;

[26]

The helmsman steered, the ship moved on;
Yet never a breeze up-blew;
The mariners all 'gan work the ropes,
Where they were wont to do;
They raised their limbs like lifeless tools—
We were a ghastly crew.

The body of my brother's son
Stood by me, knee to knee:
The body and I pulled at one rope,
But he said nought to me."

"I fear thee, ancient Mariner!"
"Be calm, thou Wedding-Guest!
'Twas not those souls that fled in pain,
Which to their corses came again,
But a troop of spirits blest:

But not by the souls of
the men, nor by
daemons of earth or
middle air, but by a
blessed troop of angelic
spirits, sent down by
the invocation of the
guardian saint.

For when it dawned—they dropped their
     arms,
And clustered round the mast;
Sweet sounds rose slowly through their
     mouths,
And from their bodies passed.

Around, around, flew each sweet sound,
Then darted to the Sun;
Slowly the sounds came back again,
Now mixed, now one by one.

Sometimes a-dropping from the sky
I heard the skylark sing;
Sometimes all little birds that are,
How they seemed to fill the sea and air
With their sweet jargoning!

And now 'twas like all instruments,
Now like a lonely flute;
And now it is an angel's song,
That makes the heavens be mute.

[27]

It ceased; yet still the sails made on
A pleasant noise till noon,
A noise like of a hidden brook
In the leafy month of June,
That to the sleeping woods all night
Singeth a quiet tune.

Till noon we quietly sailed on,
Yet never a breeze did breathe:
Slowly and smoothly went the ship,
Moved onward from beneath.

Under the keel nine fathom deep,
From the land of mist and snow,
The Spirit slid: and it was he
That made the ship to go.
The sails at noon left off their tune,
And the ship stood still also.

The lonesome Spirit from the South Pole carries on the ship as far as the Line, in obedience to the angelic troop, but still requireth vengeance.

The Sun, right up above the mast,
Had fixed her to the ocean:
But in a minute she 'gan stir,
With a short uneasy motion—
Backwards and forwards half her length
With a short uneasy motion.

Then like a pawing horse let go,
She made a sudden bound:
It flung the blood into my head,
And I fell down in a swound.

How long in that same fit I lay,
I have not to declare;
But ere my living life returned,
I heard and in my soul discerned
Two voices in the air.

The Polar Spirit's fellow-daemons, the invisible inhabitants of the element, take part in his wrong; and two of them relate, one to the other, that penance long and heavy for the ancient Mariner hath been accorded to the Polar Spirit, who returneth southward.

'Is it he?' quoth one, 'is this the man?
By him who died on cross,
With his cruel bow he laid full low
The harmless Albatross.

[28]

The Spirit who bideth by himself
In the land of mist and snow,
He loved the bird that loved the man
Who shot him with his bow.'

The other was a softer voice,
As soft as honey-dew;
Quoth he, 'The man hath penance done,
And penance more will do.' "

Part VI

FIRST VOICE:

" 'But tell me, tell me! speak again,
Thy soft response renewing—
What makes that ship drive on so fast?
What is the ocean doing?'

SECOND VOICE:

'Still as a slave before his lord,
The ocean hath no blast;
His great bright eye most silently
Up to the Moon is cast—

If he may know which way to go;
For she guides him smooth or grim.
See, brother, see! how graciously
She looketh down on him.'

FIRST VOICE:

'But why drives on that ship so fast,
Without or wave or wind?'

SECOND VOICE:

'The air is cut away before,
And closes from behind.

The Mariner hath
been cast into a trance;
for the angelic power
causeth the vessel to
drive northward faster
than human life could
endure.

[29]

Fly, brother, fly! more high, more high!
Or we shall be belated:
For slow and slow that ship will go,
When the Mariner's trance is abated.'

I woke, and we were sailing on
As in a gentle weather:
'Twas night, calm night, the moon was high;
The dead men stood together.

The supernatural motion is retarded; the Mariner awakes, and his penance begins anew.

All stood together on the deck,
For a charnel-dungeon fitter:
All fixed on me their stony eyes,
That in the Moon did glitter.

The pang, the curse, with which they died,
Had never passed away:
I could not draw my eyes from theirs,
Nor turn them up to pray.

And now this spell was snapt: once more
I viewed the ocean green,
And looked far forth, yet little saw
Of what had else been seen—

The curse is finally expiated.

Like one that on a lonesome road
Doth walk in fear and dread,
And having once turned round walks on,
And turns no more his head;
Because he knows a frightful fiend
Doth close behind him tread.

But soon there breathed a wind on me,
Nor sound nor motion made:
Its path was not upon the sea,
In ripple or in shade.

It raised my hair, it fanned my cheek
Like a meadow-gale of spring—

It mingled strangely with my fears,
Yet she sailed softly too:

Swiftly, swiftly flew the ship,
Yet she sailed softly too:
Sweetly, sweetly blew the breeze—
On me alone it blew.

Oh! dream of joy! is this indeed
The lighthouse top I see?
Is this the hill? is this the kirk?
Is this mine own countree?

We drifted o'er the harbor-bar,
And I with sobs did pray—
O let me be awake, my God!
Or let me sleep alway.

The harbor-bay was clear as glass,
So smoothly it was strewn!
And on the bay the moonlight lay,
And the shadow of the Moon.

The rock shone bright, the kirk no less,
That stands above the rock:
The moonlight steep'd in silentness
The steady weathercock.

And the bay was white with silent light,
Till rising from the same,
Full many shapes, that shadows were,
In crimson colors came.

A little distance from the prow
Those crimson shadows were:
I turned my eyes upon the deck—
Oh, Christ! what saw I there!

Each corse lay flat, lifeless and flat,
And, by the holy rood!

And the ancient Mariner beholdeth his native country.

The angelic spirits leave the dead bodies,

And appear on their own forms of light.

[31]

A man all light, a seraph-man,
On every corse there stood.

This seraph-band, each waved his hand:
It was a heavenly sight!
They stood as signals to the land,
Each one a lovely light;

This seraph-band, each waved his hand,
No voice did they impart—
No voice; but oh! the silence sank
Like music on my heart.

But soon I heard the dash of oars,
I heard the Pilot's cheer;
My head was turned perforce **away**,
And I saw a boat appear.

The Pilot and the Pilot's boy,
I heard them coming fast:
Dear Lord in Heaven! it was a joy
The dead men could not blast.

I saw a third—I heard his voice:
It is the Hermit good!
He singeth loud his godly hymns
That he makes in the wood.
He'll shrive my soul, he'll wash away
The Albatross's blood."

PART VII

"This Hermit good lives in that wood   The Hermit of the
Which slopes down to the sea.   Wood.
How loudly his sweet voice he rears!
He loves to talk with marineres
That come from a far countree.

shrive: forgive

[32]

He kneels at morn, and noon, and eve—
He hath a cushion plump:
It is the moss that wholly hides
The rotted old oak-stump.

The skiff-boat neared: I heard them talk,
'Why, this is strange, I trow!
Where are those lights so many and fair,
That signal made but now?'

Approacheth the ship with wonder.

'Strange, by my faith!' the Hermit said—
'And they answer'd not our cheer!
The planks look warp'd! and see those sails,
How thin they are and sere!
I never saw aught like to them,
Unless perchance it were

Brown skeletons of leaves that lag
My forest-brook along;
When the ivy-tod is heavy with snow,
And the owlet whoops to the wolf below,
That eats the she-wolf's young.'

'Dear Lord! it hath a fiendish look'—
(The Pilot made reply)
'I am a-fear'd.'—'Push on, push on!'
Said the Hermit cheerily.

The boat came closer to the ship,
But I nor spake nor stirred;
The boat came close beneath the ship,
And straight a sound was heard.

Under the water it rumbled on,
Still louder and more dread:
It reached the ship, it split the bay;
The ship went down like lead.

The ship suddenly sinketh.

ivy-tod: ivy plant

[33]

Stunned by that loud and dreadful sound,
Which sky and ocean smote,
Like one that hath been seven days drowned
My body lay afloat;
But swift as dreams, myself I found
Within the Pilot's boat.

The ancient Mariner is
saved in the Pilot's
boat.

Upon the whirl, where sank the ship,
The boat spun round and round;
And all was still, save that the hill
Was telling of the sound.

I moved my lips—the Pilot shrieked
And fell down in a fit;
The holy Hermit raised his eyes,
And prayed where he did sit.

I took the oars: the Pilot's boy,
Who now doth crazy go,
Laughed loud and long, and all the while
His eyes went to and fro.
'Ha! ha!' quoth he, 'full plain I see
The Devil knows how to row.'

And now, all in my own countree,
I stood on the firm land!
The Hermit stepped forth from the boat,
And scarcely he could stand.

'O shrive me, shrive me, holy man!'
The Hermit crossed his brow.
'Say quick,' quoth he, 'I bid thee say—
What manner of man art thou?'

The ancient Mariner
earnestly entreateth the
Hermit to shrive him;
and the penance of life
falls on him.

Forthwith this frame of mine was wrenched
With a woful agony,
Which forced me to begin my tale;
And then it left me free.

Since then, at an uncertain hour,
That agony returns:
And till my ghastly tale is told,
This heart within me burns.

I pass, like night, from land to land;
I have strange power of speech;
That moment that his face I see,
I know the man that must hear me;
To him my tale I teach.

What loud uproar bursts from that door!
The wedding-guests are there:
But in the garden-bower the bride
And the bride-maids singing are:
And hark, the little vesper bell,
Which biddeth me to prayer!

O Wedding-Guest! this soul hath been
Alone on a wide wide sea:
So lonely 'twas, that God Himself
Scarce seemèd there to be.

O sweeter than the marriage-feast,
'Tis sweeter far to me,
To walk together to the kirk
With a goodly company!—

To walk together to the kirk,
And all together pray,
While each to his great Father bends,
Old men, and babes, and loving friends
And youths and maidens gay!

Farewell, farewell! but this I tell
To thee, thou Wedding-Guest!
He prayeth well, who loveth well
Both man and bird and beast.

[35]

He prayeth best, who loveth best
All things both great and small;
For the dear God who loveth us,
He made and loveth all."

The Mariner, whose eye is bright,
Whose beard with age is hoar,
Is gone: and now the Wedding-Guest
Turned from the bridegroom's door.

He went like one that hath been stunned,
And is of sense forlorn:
A sadder and a wiser man
He rose the morrow morn.

¶ Here is a poem by a modern American poet. It seems
interesting to read it right after "The Rime of the Ancient
Mariner," because its tone of voice is so different.

CAPTAIN CARPENTER

John Crowe Ransom (1888–   )

Captain Carpenter rose up in his prime
Put on his pistols and went riding out
But had got wellnigh nowhere at that time
Till he fell in with ladies in a rout.

It was a pretty lady and all her train
That played with him so sweetly but before
An hour she'd taken a sword with all her main
And twined him of his nose for evermore.

[36]

Captain Carpenter mounted up one day
And rode straightway into a stranger rogue
That looked unchristian but be that as may
The Captain did not wait upon prologue.

But drew upon him out of his great heart
The other swung against him with a club
And cracked his two legs at the shinny part
And let him roll and stick like any tub.

Captain Carpenter rode many a time
From male and female took he sundry harms
He met the wife of Satan crying "I'm
The she-wolf bids you shall bear no more arms."

Their strokes and counters whistled in the wind
I wish he had delivered half his blows
But where she should have made off like a hind
The bitch bit off his arms at the elbows.

And Captain Carpenter parted with his ears
To a black devil that used him in this wise
O Jesus ere his threescore and ten years
Another had plucked out his sweet blue eyes.

Captain Carpenter got up on his roan
And sallied from the gate in hell's despite
I heard him asking in the grimmest tone
If any enemy yet there was to fight?

"To any adversary it is fame
If he risk to be wounded by my tongue
Or burnt in two beneath my red heart's flame
Such are the perils he is cast among.

"But if he can he has a pretty choice
From an anatomy with little to lose
Whether he cut my tongue and take my voice
Or whether it be my round red heart he choose."

It was the neatest knave that ever was seen
Stepping in perfume from his lady's bower
Who at this word put in his merry mien
And fell on Captain Carpenter like a tower.

I would not knock old fellows in the dust
But there lay Captain Carpenter on his back
His weapons were the old heart in his bust
And a blade shook between rotten teeth alack.

The rogue in scarlet and gray soon knew his mind
He wished to get his trophy and depart
With gentle apology and touch refined
He pierced him and produced the Captain's heart.

God's mercy rest on Captain Carpenter now
I thought him Sirs an honest gentleman
Citizen husband soldier and scholar enow
Let jangling kites eat of him if they can.

But God's deep curses follow after those
That shore him of his goodly nose and ears
His legs and strong arms at the two elbows
And eyes that had not watered seventy years

The curse of hell upon the sleek upstart
That got the Captain finally on his back
And took the red red vitals of his heart
And made the kites to whet their beaks clack clack.

¶ Another kind of story-poem is the dramatic monologue,
in which a speaker tells a tale or reveals character. Robert
Browning is particularly well known for this sort of poem.

MY LAST DUCHESS

Robert Browning (1812–1889)

That's my last Duchess painted on the wall,
Looking as if she were alive. I call
That piece a wonder, now: Frà Pandolf's hands
Worked busily a day, and there she stands.
Will't please you sit and look at her? I said
'Frà Pandolf' by design, for never read
Strangers like you that pictured countenance,
The depth and passion of its earnest glance,
But to myself they turned (since none puts by
The curtain I have drawn for you, but I)
And seemed as they would ask me, if they durst,
How such a glance came there; so, not the first
Are you to turn and ask thus. Sir, 't was not
Her husband's presence only, called that spot
Of joy into the Duchess' cheek: perhaps
Frà Pandolf chanced to say, 'Her mantle laps
Over my lady's wrist too much,' or 'Paint
Must never hope to reproduce the faint
Half-flush that dies along her throat;' such stuff
Was courtesy, she thought, and cause enough
For calling up that spot of joy. She had
A heart—how shall I say?—too soon made glad,
Too easily impressed; she liked whate'er
She looked on, and her looks went everywhere.
Sir, 't was all one! My favor at her breast,
The dropping of the daylight in the West,
The bough of cherries some officious fool
Broke in the orchard for her, the white mule
She rode with round the terrace—all and each
Would draw from her alike the approving speech,
Or blush, at least. She thanked men,—good! but thanked
Somehow—I know not how—as if she ranked

My gift of a nine-hundred-years-old name
With anybody's gift. Who'd stoop to blame
This sort of trifling? Even had you skill
In speech—(which I have not)—to make your will
Quite clear to such an one, and say, 'Just this
Or that in you disgusts me; here you miss,
Or there exceed the mark'—and if she let
Herself be lessoned so, nor plainly set
Her wits to yours, forsooth, and made excuse,
—E'en then would be some stooping, and I choose
Never to stoop. Oh, sir, she smiled, no doubt,
Whene'er I passed her; but who passed without
Much the same smile? This grew; I gave commands;
Then all smiles stopped together. There she stands
As if alive. Will 't please you rise? We'll meet
The company below then. I repeat,
The Count your master's known munificence
Is ample warrant that no just pretense
Of mine for dowry will be disallowed;
Though his fair daughter's self, as I avowed
At starting, is my object. Nay, we'll go
Together down, sir. Notice Neptune, though,
Taming a sea-horse, thought a rarity,
Which Claus of Innsbruck cast in bronze for me!

ULYSSES

Alfred, Lord Tennyson (1809–1892)

 මංශ

It little profits that an idle king,
By this still hearth, among these barren crags,
Matched with an aged wife, I mete and dole
Unequal laws unto a savage race,
That hoard, and sleep, and feed, and know not me.

I cannot rest from travel: I will drink
Life to the lees. All times I have enjoyed
Greatly, have suffered greatly, both with those
That loved me, and alone; on shore, and when
Through scudding drifts the rainy Hyades
Vext the dim sea. I am become a name
For always roaming with a hungry heart;
Much have I seen and known,—cities of men
And manners, climates, councils, governments,
Myself not least, but honored of them all;
And drunk delight of battle with my peers,
Far on the ringing plains of windy Troy.
I am a part of all that I have met;
Yet all experience is an arch wherethrough
Gleams that untraveled world whose margin fades
Forever and forever when I move.
How dull it is to pause, to make an end,
To rust unburnished, not to shine in use!
As though to breathe were life. Life piled on life
Were all too little, and of one to me
Little remains: but every hour is saved
From that eternal silence, something more,
A bringer of new things; and vile it were
For some three suns to store and hoard myself,
And this gray spirit yearning in desire
To follow knowledge like a sinking star,
Beyond the utmost bound of human thought.

This is my son, mine own Telemachus,
To whom I leave the sceptre and the isle—
Well-loved of me, discerning to fulfill
This labor, by slow prudence to make mild
A rugged people, and through soft degrees
Subdue them to the useful and the good.
Most blameless is he, centered in the sphere
Of common duties, decent not to fail
In offices of tenderness, and pay
Meet adoration to my household gods,
When I am gone. He works his work, I mine.

There lies the port; the vessel puffs her sail:
There gloom the dark, broad seas. My mariners,
Souls that have toiled, and wrought, and thought with me—
That ever with a frolic welcome took
The thunder and the sunshine, and opposed
Free hearts, free foreheads—you and I are old;
Old age hath yet his honor and his toil.
Death closes all: but something ere the end,
Some work of noble note, may yet be done,
Not unbecoming men that strove with Gods.
The lights begin to twinkle from the rocks:
The long day wanes: the slow moon climbs: the deep
Moans round with many voices. Come, my friends,
'Tis not too late to seek a newer world.
Push off, and sitting well in order smite
The sounding furrows; for my purpose holds
To sail beyond the sunset, and the baths
Of all the western stars, until I die.

It may be that the gulfs will wash us down:
It may be we shall touch the Happy Isles,
And see the great Achilles, whom we knew.
Though much is taken, much abides; and though
We are not now that strength which in old days
Moved earth and heaven; that which we are, we are;
One equal temper of heroic hearts,
Made weak by time and fate, but strong in will
To strive, to seek, to find, and not to yield.

¶ There are all sorts of narratives in poetry. T. S. Eliot's
"Journey of the Magi" is spoken by one of the wise men
after he has returned from Bethlehem to his own country.

JOURNEY OF THE MAGI

T. S. Eliot (1888–)

ﻰﺑﻭ ﻭﻊﻳ

A cold coming we had of it,
Just the worst time of the year
For a journey, and such a long journey:
The ways deep and the weather sharp,
The very dead of winter.
And the camels galled, sore-footed, refractory,
Lying down in the melting snow.
There were times we regretted
The summer palaces on slopes, the terraces,
And the silken girls bringing sherbert.
Then the camel men cursing and grumbling
And running away, and wanting their liquor and women,
And the night-fires going out, and the lack of shelters,
And the cities hostile and the towns unfriendly
And the villages dirty and charging high prices:
A hard time we had of it.·
At the end we preferred to travel all night,
Sleeping in snatches,
With the voices singing in our ears, saying
That this was all folly.
Then at dawn we came down to a temperate valley,
Wet, below the snow line, smelling of vegetation;
With a running stream and a water-mill beating the darkness,
And three trees on the low sky,
And an old white horse galloped away in the meadow.
Then we came to a tavern with vine-leaves over the lintel,
Six hands at an open door dicing for pieces of silver,
And feet kicking the empty wine-skins.
But there was no information, and so we continued
And arrived at evening, not a moment too soon
Finding the place; it was (you may say) satisfactory.

[43]

All this was a long time ago, I remember,
And I would do it again, but set down
This set down
This: were we led all that way for
Birth or Death? There was a Birth, certainly,
We had evidence and no doubt. I had seen birth and death,
But had thought they were different; this Birth was
Hard and bitter agony for us, like Death, our death.
We returned to our places, these Kingdoms,
But no longer at ease here, in the old dispensation,
With an alien people clutching their gods.
I should be glad of another death.

¶ The Magus who is speaking has died to his old life, spiritually, because he has had a vision of the truth in Jesus. But revelation is painful, and he is ready to die bodily. Through the Magus, Eliot, himself a convert, indicates the difficulties of being a convert.

   W. H. Auden wrote the next poem for the sound-track of a film about the British postal service.

NIGHT MAIL

W. H. Auden (1907–   )

ঙ~ ঙ

This is the night mail crossing the border,
Bringing the cheque and the postal order,
Letters for the rich, letters for the poor,
The shop at the corner, and the girl next door.
Pulling up Beattock, a steady climb—
The gradient's against her but she's on time.

[44]

Past cotton grass and moorland boulder,
Shovelling white steam over her shoulder,
Snorting noisily as she passes
Silent miles of wind-swept grasses;
Birds turn their heads as she approaches,
Stare from the bushes at her blank-faced coaches;

Sheep dogs cannot turn her course,
They slumber on with paws across.
In the farm she passes no one wakes,
But a jug in the bedroom gently shakes.

Dawn freshens, the climb is done.
Down towards Glasgow she descends
Towards the steam tugs yelping down the glade of cranes,
Towards the fields of apparatus, the furnaces
Set on the dark plain like gigantic chessmen.
All Scotland waits for her:
In the dark glens, beside the pale-green sea lochs,
Men long for news.

Letters of thanks, letters from banks,
Letters of joy from the girl and boy,
Receipted bills and invitations
To inspect new stock or visit relations,
And applications for situations,
And timid lovers' declarations,
And gossip, gossip from all the nations,
News circumstantial, news financial,
Letters with holiday snaps to enlarge in,
Letters with faces scrawled in the margin.

Letters from uncles, cousins and aunts,
Letters to Scotland from the south of France,
Letters of condolence to Highlands and Lowlands,
Notes from overseas to the Hebrides;
Written on paper of every hue,
The pink, the violet, the white and the blue;
The chatty, the catty, the boring, adoring,

The cold and official and the heart's outpouring,
Clever, stupid, short and long,
The typed and the printed and the spelt all wrong.

Thousands are still asleep
Dreaming of terrifying monsters,
Or a friendly tea beside the band at Cranston's or Crawford's;
Asleep in working Glasgow, asleep in well-set Edinburgh,
Asleep in granite Aberdeen.
They continue their dreams
But shall wake soon and long for letters.
And none shall hear the postman's knock
Without a quickening of the heart,
For who can bear to feel himself forgotten?

¶ Little poems can tell stories, too. More likely they tell you about a person, or relate an anecdote which illustrates something universal.

PIAZZA PIECE

John Crowe Ransom (1888–   )

—I am a gentleman in a dustcoat trying
To make you hear. Your ears are soft and small
And listen to an old man not at all;
They want the young men's whispering and sighing.
But see the roses on your trellis dying
And hear the spectral singing of the moon—
For I must have my lovely lady soon.
I am a gentleman in a dustcoat trying.

[46]

—I am a lady young in beauty waiting
Until my truelove comes, and then we kiss.
But what gray man among the vines is this
Whose words are dry and faint as in a dream?
Back from my trellis, sir, before I scream!
I am a lady young in beauty waiting.

THE MILL

Edwin Arlington Robinson (1869–1935)

ॐ❧ ☙

The miller's wife had waited long,
    The tea was cold, the fire was dead:
And there might yet be nothing wrong
    In how he went and what he said:
"There are no millers any more,"
    Was all that she had heard him say;
And he had lingered at the door
    So long that it seemed yesterday.

Sick with a fear that had no form
    She knew that she was there at last;
And in the mill there was a warm
    And mealy fragrance of the past.
What else there was would only seem
    To say again what he had meant;
And what was hanging from a beam
    Would not have heeded where she went.

And if she thought it followed her,
    She may have reasoned in the dark
That one way of the few there were
    Would hide her and would leave no mark:
Black water, smooth above the weir
    Like starry velvet in the night,

Though ruffled once, would soon appear
The same as ever to the sight.

THE END OF THE WORLD

Archibald Macleish (1892–   )

ဆာ ⚬⚬

Quite unexpectedly as Vasserot
The armless ambidextrian was lighting
A match between his great and second toe
And Ralph the lion was engaged in biting
The neck of Madame Sossman while the drum
Pointed, and Teeny was about to cough
In waltz-time swinging Jocko by the thumb—
Quite unexpectedly the top blew off:
And there, there overhead, there, there, hung over
Those thousands of white faces, those dazed eyes,
There in the starless dark, the poise, the hover,
There with vast wings across the canceled skies,
There in the sudden blackness, the black pall
Of nothing, nothing, nothing—nothing at all.

LUCIFER IN STARLIGHT

George Meredith (1828–1909)

ဆာ ⚬⚬

On a starr'd night Prince Lucifer uprose.
   Tired of his dark dominion swung the fiend
   Above the rolling ball in cloud part screen'd,
Where sinners hugg'd their spectre of repose.

Poor prey to his hot fit of pride were those.
  And now upon his western wing he lean'd,
Now his huge bulk o'er Afric's sands careen'd,
Now the black planet shadow'd Arctic snows.
Soaring through wider zones that prick'd his scars
  With memory of the old revolt from Awe,
He reach'd a middle height, and at the stars,
Which are the brain of heaven, he look'd, and sank.
Around the ancient track march'd, rank on rank,
  The army of unalterable law.

¶ The best creator of character in English poetry—if you except Shakespeare in his plays—was the first English poet, Geoffrey Chaucer. The character sketches which follow all come from the "Prologue" to the *Canterbury Tales*, done into modern English by Neville Coghill. Actually Chaucer's language is not very difficult, and when you begin to read more poetry you must read Chaucer in the original.

If you think you notice any traces of sarcasm in some of these sketches, you will undoubtedly be right.

TEN OF CHAUCER'S PEOPLE

Geoffrey Chaucer (1340?–1400)

 famma

A Perfect Knight

There was a *Knight*, a most distinguished man,
Who from the day on which he first began
To ride abroad had followed chivalry,
Truth, honor, greatness of heart and courtesy.

[49]

He had done nobly in his sovereign's war
And ridden into battle, no man more,
As well in christian as in heathen places,
And ever honored for his noble graces.

. . .

In fifteen mortal battles he had been
And jousted for our faith at Tramissene
Thrice in the lists, and always killed his man.
This same distinguished knight had led the van
Once with the Bey of Balat, doing work
For him against another heathen Turk;
He was of sovereign value in all eyes.
And though so much distinguished, he was wise
And in his bearing modest as a maid.
He never yet a boorish thing had said
In all his life to any, come what might;
He was a true, a perfect gentle-knight.

A POLITE NUN

Simple her way of smiling was and coy.
Her greatest oath was only "By St. Loy."
And she was known as Madam Eglantyne.
And well she sang a service, with a fine
Intoning through her nose, as was most seemly,
And she spoke daintily in French, extremely,
After the school of Stratford-atte-Bowe;
French in the Paris style she did not know.
At meat her manners were well taught withal;
No morsel from her lips did she let fall,
Nor dipped her fingers in the sauce too deep;
But she could carry a morsel up and keep.
The smallest drop from falling on her breast.
For courtliness she had a special zest.
And she would wipe her upper lip so clean
That not a trace of grease was to be seen
Upon the cup when she had drunk; to eat,
She reached a hand sedately for the meat.

[50]

A Sporting Monk

There was a *Monk*, a leader of the fashions;
Inspecting farms and hunting were his passions,
A manly man, to be an Abbot able,
Many a dainty horse he had in stable;
His bridle, when he rode, a man might hear
Jingling in a whistling wind as clear,
Aye, and as loud as does the chapel bell
Where my lord Monk was Prior of the cell.

.   .   .

This Monk was therefore a good man to horse;
Greyhounds he had, as swift as birds, to course.
Hunting a hare or riding at a fence
Was all his fun, he spared for no expense.
I saw his sleeves were garnished at the hand
With fine gray fur, the finest in the land,
And where his hood was fastened at the chin
He had a wrought-gold cunningly fashioned pin;
Into a lover's knot it seemed to pass.
His head was bald and shone—as any glass,
So did his face, as if it had been greased.
He was a fat and personable priest;
His bright eyes rolled, they never seemed to settle,
They glittered like the flames beneath a kettle;
Supple his boots, his horse in fine condition.
He was a prelate fit for exhibition,
He was not pale like a tormented soul.
He liked a fat swan best, and roasted whole.

A Greedy Friar

Highly beloved and intimate was he
With County folk wherever he might be,
And worthy city women with possessions;
For he was qualified to hear confessions,
Or so he said, with more than priestly scope;
He had a special license from the Pope.

[51]

Sweetly he heard his penitents at shrift
With pleasant absolution, for a gift.
He was an easy man in penance-giving
Where he could hope to make a decent living;
It's a sure sign whenever gifts are given
To a poor Order that a man's well shriven,
And should he give enough he knew in verity
The penitent repented in sincerity.
For many a fellow is so hard of heart
He cannot weep, for all his inward smart.
Therefore instead of weeping and of prayer
One should give silver for a poor Friar's care.

A GLUTTONOUS RICH MAN

His house was never short of bake-meat pies,
Of fish and flesh, and these in such supplies
It positively snowed with meat and drink
And all the dainties that a man could think.
According to the seasons of the year
Changes of dish were ordered to appear.
He kept fat partridges in coops, beyond,
Many a bream and pike were in his pond.
Woe to the cook whose sauces had no sting
Or who was unprepared in anything!
And in his hall a table stood arrayed
And ready all day long, with places laid.

A TASTY COOK

They had a *Cook* with them who stood alone
For boiling chicken with a marrow-bone,
Sharp flavoring-powder and a spice for savor.
He could distinguish London ale by flavor,
And he could roast and seethe and broil and fry,
Make good thick soup and bake a tasty pie.
But a great pity, as it seemed to me
Was that he had an ulcer on his knee.

[52]

THE WIFE OF BATH

In all the parish not a dame dared stir
Towards the altar steps in front of her,
And if indeed they did, so wrath was she
As to be quite put out of charity.
Her kerchiefs were of finely woven ground;
I dared have sworn they weighed a good ten pound,
The ones she wore on Sunday, on her head.
Her hose were of the finest scarlet red
And gartered tight; her shoes were soft and new.
Bold was her face, handsome, and red in hue.
A worthy woman all her life, what's more
She'd had five husbands, all at the church door,
Apart from other company in youth;
No need just now to speak of that, forsooth.

A PARSON

Wide was his parish, with houses far asunder,
Yet he neglected not in rain or thunder,
In sickness or in grief, to pay a call
On the remotest whether great or small,
Upon his feet, and in his hand a stave.
This noble example to his sheep he gave,
First following the word before he taught it,
And it was from the gospel he had caught it.
This little proverb he would add thereto
That if gold rust, what then will iron do?
For if a priest be foul in whom we trust
No wonder that a common man should rust;

. . .

The true example that a priest should give
Is one of cleanness, how the sheep should live.
He did not set his benefice to hire
And leave his sheep encumbered in the mire
Or run to London to earn easy bread
By singing masses for the wealthy dead.

[53]

A Stout Miller

The *Miller* was a chap of sixteen stone,
A great stout fellow big in brawn and bone.
He did well out of them, for he could go
And win the ram at any wrestling show.
Broad, knotty and short-shouldered, he would boast
He could heave any door off hinge and post,
Or take a run and break it with his head.
His beard, like any sow or fox, was red
And broad as well, as though it were a spade;
And, at its very tip, his nose displayed
A wart on which there stood a tuft of hair
Red as the bristles in an old sow's ear.

His nostrils were as black as they were wide.
He had a sword and buckler at his side,
His mighty mouth was like a furnace door.
A wrangler and buffoon, he had a store
Of tavern stories, filthy in the main.
His was a master-hand at stealing grain.

A Girlish Pardoner

This *Pardoner* had hair as yellow as wax,
Hanging down smoothly like a hank of flax.
In driblets fell his locks behind his head
Down to his shoulders which they overspread;
Thinly they fell, like rat-tails, one by one.
He wore no hood upon his head, for fun;
The hood inside his wallet had been stowed,
He aimed at riding in the latest mode;
But for a little cap his head was bare
And he had bulging eye-balls, like a hare.
He'd sewed a holy relic on his cap;
His wallet lay before him on his lap,
Brimful of pardons come from Rome all hot.

pardoner: seller of pardons for sins against God.

[54]

He had the same small voice a goat has got.
His chin no beard had harbored, nor would harbor,
Smoother than ever chin was left by barber.

¶ The first good poet in English after Chaucer was a
lively laureate named John Skelton. He invented a way of
writing in short lines, rhymed many times in a row, which
has never been done well after him, and which is called
"skeltonics."

TO MISTRESS MARGARET HUSSEY

John Skelton (1460?–1529)

Merry Margaret,
As midsummer flower,
Gentle as falcon
Or hawk of the tower;
With solace and gladness,
Much mirth and no madness,
All good and no badness;
So joyously,
So maidenly,
So womanly,
Her demeaning
In everything
Far, far passing
That I can indite,
Or suffice to write
Of Merry Margaret,
As midsummer flower,
Gentle as falcon

[55]

Or hawk of the tower.
As patient and as still,
And as full of good will,
As the fair Isaphill,
Coliander,
Sweet pomander,
Good Cassander;
Steadfast of thought,
Well made, well wrought.
Far may be sought
Ere than ye can find
So courteous, so kind,
As Merry Margaret,
This midsummer flower,
Gentle as falcon
Or hawk of the tower.

¶ Here is another old poem, a self-portrait of an inmate of Bedlam, London's famous insane asylum. The author is unknown.

TOM O'BEDLAM'S SONG

Anonymous

From the hag and hungry goblin
That into rags would rend ye
And the spirit that stands by the naked man
In the Book of Moons defend ye!
That of your five sound senses
You never be forsaken
Nor wander from your selves with Tom
Abroad to beg your bacon.

While I do sing "Any food, any feeding,
Feeding, drink, or clothing."
Come dame or maid, be not afraid,
Poor Tom will injure nothing. . . .

With a thought I took for Maudlin
And a cruse of cockle pottage,
With a thing thus tall, sky bless you all,
I befell into this dotage.
I slept not since the Conquest,
Till then I never waked
Till the roguish boy of love where I lay
Me found and stripped me naked.
    And now I sing "Any food, any feeding,
    Feeding, drink, or clothing."
    Come dame or maid, be not afraid,
    Poor Tom will injure nothing. . . .

When I short have shorn my sour face
And swigged my horny barrel
In an oaken inn I pound my skin
As a suit of gilt apparel.
The moon's my constant Mistress
And the lowly owl my marrow;
The flaming Drake and the Nightcrow make
Me music to my sorrow.
    While I do sing "Any food, any feeding,
    Feeding, drink, or clothing."
    Come dame or maid, be not afraid,
    Poor Tom will injure nothing. . . .

I know more than Apollo,
For oft when he lies sleeping
I see the stars at bloody wars
In the wounded wellkin weeping,
The moon embrace her shepherd
And the queen of Love her warrior,

cruse: bowl   *cockle:* a mussel or mollusc
conquest: Norman Conquest, 1066 A.D.   *marrow:* companion
wellkin: sky

[57]

While the first doth horn the star of morn
And the next the heavenly Farrier,
    While I do sing "Any food, any feeding,
    Feeding, drink, or clothing."
    Come dame or maid, be not afraid,
    Poor Tom will injure nothing . . .

With an host of furious fancies
Whereof I am commander,
With a burning spear, and a horse of air,
To the wilderness I wander.
By a knight of ghosts and shadows
I summoned am to tourney
Ten leagues beyond the wide world's end,
Me thinks it is no journey.
    Yet will I sing "Any food, any feeding,
    Feeding, drink, or clothing."
    Come dame or maid, be not afraid,
    Poor Tom will injure nothing.

¶ Here is another kind of writing entirely, still at the service of portraiture. Ben Jonson had command of a greater variety of lines and poetic styles than Shakespeare himself.

"STILL TO BE NEAT"

Ben Jonson (1573–1637)

ह‌ॐ ॐड़

Still to be neat, still to be drest
As you were going to a feast;
Still to be powder'd, still perfum'd:
Lady, it is to be presumed,

Farrier: blacksmith

Though art's hid causes are not found,
All is not sweet, all is not sound.

Give me a look, give me a face
That makes simplicity a grace;
Robes loosely flowing, hair as free:
Such sweet neglect more taketh me
Than all th' adulteries of art;
They strike mine eyes, but not my heart.

ON CHARLES II

John Wilmot, Earl of Rochester (1647–1680)

᭦᭦ ᭦᭦

Here lies a Great and Mighty King,
　Whose Promise none relys on,
He never said a Foolish thing
　Nor ever did a Wise one.

¶ The satirical epitaph can be a sharp instrument. So can
the extended portrait, especially in the hands of Alexander
Pope.

ATTICUS

Alexander Pope (*1688–1744*)

೪ঌ ঌ৪

Peace to all such! but were there One whose fires
True Genius kindles, and fair Fame inspires;
Blest with each talent and each art to please,
And born to write, converse, and live with ease:
Should such a man, too fond to rule alone,
Bear, like the Turk, no brother near the throne,
View him with scornful, yet with jealous eyes,
And hate for arts that caus'd himself to rise;
Damn with faint praise, assent with civil leer,
And without sneering, teach the rest to sneer;
Willing to wound, and yet afraid to strike,
Just hint a fault, and hesitate dislike;
Alike reserv'd to blame, or to commend,
A tim'rous foe, and a suspicious friend;
Dreading ev'n fools, by flatterers besieg'd,
And so obliging, that he ne'er oblig'd;
Like Cato, give his little Senate laws,
And sit attentive to his own applause;
While Wits and Templars ev'ry sentence raise,
And wonder with a foolish face of praise—
Who but must laugh, if such a man there be?
Who would not weep, if Atticus were he!

¶ Atticus was really Joseph Addison, who wrote verse and plays, but is best known for *The Spectator*.

This poem and the next are written in heroic couplets, where lines balance with lines, and half-lines with half-lines.

GEORGE VILLIERS, DUKE OF BUCKINGHAM

John Dryden (1631–1700)

A man so various, that he seemed to be
Not one, but all mankind's epitome.
Stiff in opinions, always in the wrong;
Was everything by starts, and nothing long:
But, in the course of one revolving moon,
Was chemist, fiddler, statesman, and buffoon;
Then all for women, painting, rhyming, drinking,
Besides ten thousand freaks that died in thinking.
Blest madman, who could every hour employ,
With something new to wish, or to enjoy!
Railing and praising were his usual themes;
And both (to show his judgment) in extremes:
So over violent, or over civil,
That every man, with him, was God or Devil.
In squandering wealth was his peculiar art:
Nothing went unrewarded, but desert.
Beggared by fools, whom still he found too late:
He had his jest, and they had his estate.

¶ The heroic couplet was popular in the 18th century, and it reflected the age's desire for order. In America in the 19th century, we come to another extreme with Walt Whitman. This poem comes out of his experiences as a male nurse in the Civil War.

---

desert: what deserves reward.

[61]

A SIGHT IN CAMP IN THE DAYBREAK GRAY AND DIM

Walt Whitman (1819–1892)

A sight in camp in the daybreak gray and dim,
As from my tent I emerge so early sleepless,
As slow I walk in the cool fresh air the path near by the hos-
  pital tent,
Three forms I see on stretchers lying, brought out there un-
  tended lying,
Over each the blanket spread, ample brownish woolen blanket,
Gray and heavy blanket, folding, covering all.

Curious I halt and silent stand,
Then with light fingers I from the face of the nearest the first
  just lift the blanket;
Who are you elderly man so gaunt and grim, with well-gray'd
  hair, and flesh all sunken about the eyes?
Who are you my dear comrade?

Then to the second I step—and who are you my child and
  darling?
Who are you sweet boy with cheeks yet blooming?
Then to the third—a face nor child nor old, very calm, as of
  beautiful yellow-white ivory;
Young man I think I know you—I think this face is the face of
  the Christ himself,
Dead and divine and brother of all, and here again he lies.

¶ There is a quietness, a lack of strain, in Whitman, which
is shocking after the cleverness of Pope and Dryden. His
best poems are long and are not included in this book, and
the reader must come to them later.

MINIVER CHEEVY

Edwin Arlington Robinson (1869–1935)

৪৯ ৩৯

Miniver Cheevy, child of scorn,
    Grew lean while he assailed the seasons;
He wept that he was ever born,
    And he had reasons.

Miniver loved the days of old
    When swords were bright and steeds were prancing;
The vision of a warrior bold
    Would set him dancing.

Miniver sighed for what was not,
    And dreamed, and rested from his labors;
He dreamed of Thebes and Camelot,
    And Priam's neighbors.

Miniver mourned the ripe renown
    That made so many a name so fragrant;
He mourned Romance, now on the town,
    And Art, a vagrant.

Miniver loved the Medici,
    Albeit he had never seen one;
He would have sinned incessantly
    Could he have been one.

Miniver cursed the commonplace
    And eyed a khaki suit with loathing;
He missed the mediaeval grace
    Of iron clothing.

Miniver scorned the gold he sought,
    But sore annoyed was he without it;

[63]

Miniver thought, and thought, and thought,
    And thought about it.

Miniver Cheevy, born too late,
    Scratched his head and kept on thinking;
Miniver coughed and called it fate,
    And kept on drinking.

MR. FLOOD'S PARTY

Edwin Arlington Robinson (1869–1935)

ঽৡ ৶ঽ

Old Eben Flood, climbing alone one night
Over the hill between the town below
And the forsaken upland hermitage
That held as much as he should ever know
On earth again of home, paused warily.
The road was his with not a native near;
And Eben, having leisure, said aloud,
For no man else in Tilbury Town to hear:

"Well, Mr. Flood, we have the harvest moon
Again, and we may not have many more;
The bird is on the wing, the poet says,
And you and I have said it here before.
Drink to the bird." He raised up to the light
The jug that he had gone so far to fill,
And answered huskily: "Well, Mr. Flood,
Since you propose it, I believe I will."

Alone, as if enduring to the end
A valiant armor of scarred hopes outworn,
He stood there in the middle of the road
Like Roland's ghost winding a silent horn.

[64]

Below him, in the town among the trees,
Where friends of other days had honored him,
A phantom salutation of the dead
Rang thinly till old Eben's eyes were dim.

Then, as a mother lays her sleeping child
Down tenderly, fearing it may awake,
He set the jug down slowly at his feet
With trembling care, knowing that most things break;
And only when assured that on firm earth
It stood, as the uncertain lives of men
Assuredly did not, he paced away,
And with his hand extended paused again:

"Well, Mr. Flood, we have not met like this
In a long time; and many a change has come
To both of us, I fear, since last it was
We had a drop together. Welcome home!"
Convivially returning with himself,
Again he raised the jug up to the light;
And with an acquiescent quaver said:
"Well, Mr. Flood, if you insist, I might.

"Only a very little, Mr. Flood—
For auld lang syne. No more, sir; that will do."
So, for the time, apparently it did,
And Eben evidently thought so too;
For soon amid the silver loneliness
Of night he lifted up his voice and sang,
Secure, with only two moons listening,
Until the whole harmonious landscape rang—

"For auld lang syne." The weary throat gave out,
The last word wavered; and the song being done,
He raised again the jug regretfully
And shook his head, and was again alone.
There was not much that was ahead of him,
And there was nothing in the town below—

Where strangers would have shut the many doors
That many friends had opened long ago.

¶ E. A. Robinson did his narratives and character sketches in rhyme and meter, and wrote some of the best poems ever written by an American. At the same time Edgar Lee Masters was writing the free verse character sketches which made up his *Spoon River Anthology*. The next two poems come from that book.

ANN RUTLEDGE

Edgar Lee Masters (1869–1950)

ह‌‌‌‌‌‌‌‌

Out of me unworthy and unknown
The vibrations of deathless music:
"With malice toward none, with charity for all."
Out of me the forgiveness of millions toward millions,
And the beneficent face of a nation
Shining with justice and truth.
I am Ann Rutledge who sleep beneath these weeds,
Beloved in life of Abraham Lincoln,
Wedded to him, not through union,
But through separation.
Bloom forever, O Republic,
From the dust of my bosom!

PETIT, THE POET

Edgar Lee Masters (1869–1950)

ह•> •ई§

Seeds in a dry pod, tick, tick, tick,
Tick, tick, tick, like mites in a quarrel—
Faint iambics that the full breeze wakens—
But the pine tree makes a symphony thereof.
Triolets, villanelles, rondels, rondeaus,
Ballades by the score with the same old thought:
The snows and the roses of yesterday are vanished;
And what is love but a rose that fades?
Life all around me here in the village:
Tragedy, comedy, valor, and truth,
Courage, constancy, heroism, failure—
All in the loom, and oh what patterns!
Woodlands, meadows, streams and rivers—
Blind to all of it all my life long.
Triolets, villanelles, rondels, rondeaus,
Seeds in a dry pod, tick, tick, tick,
Tick, tick, tick, what little iambics,
While Homer and Whitman roared in the pines!

¶ T. S. Eliot has also written some portraits, though his
tone of voice differs from Masters'.

---

[67]

AUNT HELEN

T. S. Eliot (1888–   )

ౖ❧ ❧ఠ

Miss Helen Slingsby was my maiden aunt,
And lived in a small house near a fashionable square
Cared for by servants to the number of four.
Now when she died there was silence in heaven
And silence at her end of the street.
The shutters were drawn and the undertaker wiped his feet—
He was aware that this sort of thing had occurred before.
The dogs were handsomely provided for,
But shortly afterwards the parrot died too.
The Dresden clock continued ticking on the mantelpiece,
And the footman sat upon the dining-table
Holding the second housemaid on his knees—
Who had always been so careful while her mistress lived.

COUSIN NANCY

T. S. Eliot (1888–   )

ౖ❧ ❧ఠ

Miss Nancy Ellicott
Strode across the hills and broke them,
Rode across the hills and broke them—
The barren New England hills—
Riding to hounds
Over the cow-pasture.

    Miss Nancy Ellicott smoked
And danced all the modern dances;

And her aunts were not quite sure how they felt about it,
But they knew that it was modern.

    Upon the glazen shelves kept watch
Matthew and Waldo, guardians of the faith,
The army of unalterable law.

¶ Matthew is Matthew Arnold, and Waldo is Ralph Waldo Emerson—those guardians of all that is elevated and serious. If the last line seems familiar to you, you can find it on page 49, in the poem from which Eliot took it.

LADY LOST

John Crowe Ransom (1888–89)

This morning, there flew up the lane
A timid lady-bird to our bird-bath
And eyed her image dolefully as death;
This afternoon, knocked on our windowpane
To be let in from the rain.

And when I caught her eye
She looked aside, but at the clapping thunder
And sight of the whole earth blazing up like tinder
Looked in on us again most miserably,
Indeed as if she would cry.

So I will go out into the park and say,
"Who has lost a delicate brown-eyed lady
In the West End Section? Or has anybody
Injured some fine woman in some dark way.
Last night or yesterday?

[69]

"Let the owner come and claim possession,
No questions will be asked. But stroke her gently
With loving words, and she will evidently
Resume her full soft-haired white-breasted fashion,
And her right home and her right passion."

THE TWINS

Karl Shapiro (1913–)

Likeness has made them animal and shy.
See how they turn their full gaze left and right,
Seeking the other, yet not moving close;
Nothing in their relationship is gross,
But soft, conspicuous, like giraffes. And why
Do they not speak except by sudden sight?

Sisters kiss freely and unsubtle friends
Wrestle like lovers; brothers loudly laugh:
These in a dreamier bondage dare not touch.
Each is the other's soul and hears too much
The heartbeat of the other; each apprehends
The sad duality and the imperfect half.

The one lay sick, the other wandered free,
But like a child to a small plot confined
Walked a short way and dumbly reappeared.
It is not all-in-all of what they feared,
The single death, the obvious destiny
That maims the miracle their will designed?
For they go emptily from face to face,
Keeping the instinctive partnership of birth
A ponderous marriage and a sacred name;
Theirs is the pride of shouldering each the same

The old indignity of Esau's race
And Dromio's denouement of tragic mirth.

· MY PAPA'S WALTZ

Theodore Roethke (1908–   )

The whisky on your breath
Could make a small boy dizzy;
But I hung on like death:
Such waltzing was not easy.

We romped until the pans
Slid from the kitchen shelf;
My mother's countenance
Could not unfrown itself.

The hand that held my wrist
Was battered on one knuckle;
At every step you missed
My right ear scraped a buckle.

You beat time on my head
With a palm caked hard by dirt,
Then waltzed me off to bed
Still clinging to your shirt.

JOHN SUTTER

Yvor Winters (1900–   )

჻

I was the patriarch of the shining land,
Of the blond summer and metallic grain;
Men vanished at the motion of my hand,
And when I beckoned they would come again.

The earth grew dense with grain at my desire;
The shade was deepened at the springs and streams;
Moving in dust that clung like pillared fire,
The gathering herds grew heavy in my dreams.

Across the mountains, naked from the heights,
Down to the valley broken settlers came,
And in my houses feasted through the nights,
Rebuilt their sinews and assumed a name.

In my clear rivers my own men discerned
The motive for the ruin and the crime—
Gold heavier than earth, a wealth unearned,
Loot, for two decades, from the heart of Time.

Metal, intrinsic value, deep and dense,
Preanimate, inimitable, still,
Real, but an evil with no human sense,
Dispersed the mind to concentrate the will.

Grained by alchemic change, the human kind
Turned from themselves to rivers and to rocks;
With dynamite broke metal unrefined;
Measured their moods by geologic shocks.

With knives they dug the metal out of stone;
Turned rivers back, for gold through ages piled,
Drove knives to hearts, and faced the gold alone;
Valley and river ruined and reviled;

[72]

Reviled and ruined me, my servant slew,
Strangled him from the fig tree by my door.
When they had done what fury bade them do,
I was cursing a beggar, stripped and sore.

What end impersonal, what breathless age,
Incontinent of quiet and of years,
What calm catastrophe will yet assuage
This final drouth of penitential tears?

JOHN DAY, FRONTIERSMAN

Yvor Winters (1900–)

Among the first and farthest! Elk and deer
Fell as your rifle rang in rocky caves;
There your lean shadow swept the still frontier,
Your eyes regarded the Columbia's waves.

Amid the stony winter, gray with care,
Hunted by savages from sleep to sleep
—Those patriots of darkness and despair!—
You climbed in solitude what rigid steep!

Broken at last by very force of frame,
By wintry hunger like a warrior's brand,
You died a madman. And now bears your name
A gentle river in a fertile land.

The eminence is gone that met your eye;
The winding savage, too, has sunk away.
Now, like a summer myth, the meadows lie,
Deep in the calm of sylvan slow decay.

[73]

FARM BOY AFTER SUMMER

Robert Francis (1901–   )

ৡৼ ৶ৡ

A seated statue of himself he seems.
A bronze slowness becomes him. Patently
The page he contemplates he doesn't see.

The lesson, the long lesson, has been summer.
His mind holds summer as his skin holds sun.
For once the homework, all of it, was done.

What were the crops, where were the fiery fields
Where for so many days so many hours
The sun assaulted him with glittering showers?

Expect a certain absence in his presence.
Expect all winter long a summer scholar,
For scarcely all its snows can cool that color.

¶ William Carlos Williams writes about people, as he
writes about everything, with the language people really
use when they talk.

HEMMED-IN MALES

William Carlos Williams (1883–   )

ৡৼ ৶ৡ

The saloon is gone up the creek
with the black sand round its
mouth, it went floating like

[74]

a backhouse on the Mississippi in
flood time but it went up
the creek into Limbo from whence

only empty bottles ever return
and that's where George is
He's gone upstream to ask 'em

to let him in at the hole
in the wall where the W.C.T.U.
sits knitting elastic stockings

for varicose veins. Poor George
he's got a job now as janitor
in Lincoln School but the saloon

is gone forever with pictures
of Sullivan and Kilrain on
the walls and Pop Anson holding

a bat. Poor George, they've cut
out his pituitary gland and his
vas deferens is in the spitoon—

you can laugh at him without his
organs but that's the way with
a river when it wants to

drown you, it sucks you in and
you feel the old saloon sinking
under you and you say good-by

just as George did, good-by poetry
the black sand's got me, the old
days are over, there's no place

any more for me to go now
except home—

LIGHTHEARTED WILLIAM

William Carlos Williams (1883–)

ફ~ ~ફ

Lighthearted William twirled
his November moustaches
and, half dressed, looked
from the bedroom window
upon the spring weather.

Heigh-ya! sighed he gaily
leaning out to see
up and down the street
where a heavy sunlight
lay beyond some blue shadows.

Into the room he drew
his head again and laughed
to himself quietly
twirling his green moustaches.

¶ Again for contrast, see the way Goldsmith in the 18th
century treats a common subject.

THE VILLAGE SCHOOLMASTER

Oliver Goldsmith (1730–1774)

ફ~ ~ફ

Beside yon straggling fence that skirts the way,
With blossomed furze unprofitably gay,
There, in his noisy mansion, skilled to rule,

[76]

The village master taught his little school;
A man severe he was, and stern to view;
I knew him well, and every truant knew;
Well had the boding tremblers learned to trace
The day's disasters in his morning face;
Full well they laughed, with counterfeited glee,
At all his jokes, for many a joke had he;
Full well the busy whisper, circling round,
Conveyed the dismal tidings when he frowned;
Yet he was kind; or, if severe in aught,
The love he bore to learning was in fault;
The village all declared how much he knew;
'Twas certain he could write, and cipher too;
Lands he could measure, terms and tides presage,
And even the story ran that he could gauge.
In arguing, too, the parson owned his skill,
For, even though vanquished, he could argue still;
While words of learned length and thundering sound
Amazed the gazing rustics ranged around;
And still they gazed, and still the wonder grew
That one small head could carry all he knew.

¶ George Crabbe, a little later, wrote with more realism
and less decoration.

THE VILLAGE

George Crabbe (1754–1832)

୫୬ ୫୬

Fled are those times, when, in harmonious strains,
The rustic poet praised his native plains.
No shepherds now, in smooth alternate verse,

Their country's beauty or their nymphs' rehearse;
Yet still for these we frame the tender strain,
Still in our lays fond Corydons complain,
And shepherds' boys their amorous pains reveal,
The only pains, alas! they never feel.

. . .

I grant indeed that fields and flocks have charms
For him that grazes or for him that farms;
But when amid such pleasing scenes I trace
The poor laborious natives of the place,
And see the mid-day sun, with fervid ray,
On their bare heads and dewy temples play;
While some, with feebler heads and fainter hearts,
Deplore their fortune, yet sustain their parts:
Then shall I dare these real ills to hide
In tinsel trappings of poetic pride?
No; cast by Fortune on a frowning coast,
Which neither groves nor happy valleys boast;
Where other cares than those the Muse relates,
And other shepherds dwell with other mates;
By such examples taught, I paint the Cot,
As Truth will paint it, and as Bards will not:
Nor you, ye poor, of letter'd scorn complain,
To you the smoothest song is smooth in vain;
O'ercome by labor, and bow'd down by time,
Feel you the barren flattery of a rhyme?
Can poets soothe you, when you pine for bread,
By winding myrtles round your ruin'd shed?
Can their light tales your weighty griefs o'erpower,
Or glad with airy mirth the toilsome hour?
Lo! where the heath, with withering brake grown o'er.
Lends the light turf that warms the neighboring poor;
From thence a length of burning sand appears,
Where the thin harvest waves its wither'd ears;
Rank weeds, that every art and care defy,
Reign o'er the land, and rob the blighted rye:
There thistles stretch their prickly arms afar,

And to the ragged infant threaten war;
There poppies nodding, mock the hope of toil;
There the blue bugloss paints the sterile soil;
Hardy and high, above the slender sheaf,
The slimy mallow waves her silky leaf;
O'er the young shoot the charlock throws a shade,
And clasping tares cling round the sickly blade;
With mingled tints the rocky coasts abound,
And a sad splendor vainly shines around.

¶ Crabbe talks about economic fact, and writes a poetry that is fiercely anti-sentimental. Economics is not a frequent subject in English poetry, but it enters the world of William Blake. In "London" the church is blackening, not only figuratively because it is regressing morally, but literally because of the soot of the industrial revolution. It is the same period which sent the English soldier to die fighting the American colonists.

LONDON

William Blake (1757–1827)

I wander thro' each charter'd street,
Near where the charter'd Thames does flow,
And mark in every face I meet
Marks of weakness, marks of woe.

In every cry of every Man,
In every Infant's cry of fear,

In every voice, in every ban,
The mind-forg'd manacles I hear.

How the Chimney-sweeper's cry
Every black'ning Church appalls;
And the hapless Soldier's sigh
Runs in blood down Palace Walls.

But most thro' midnight streets I hear
How the youthful Harlot's curse
Blasts the new born Infant's tear,
And blights with plagues the Marriage hearse.

¶ A little later, Wordsworth can find the same city beautiful—but only when it is asleep!

UPON WESTMINSTER BRIDGE

William Wordsworth (1770–1850)

Earth has not anything to show more fair:
Dull would he be of soul who could pass by
A sight so touching in its majesty:
This city now doth, like a garment, wear
The beauty of the morning; silent, bare,
Ships, towers, domes, theaters, and temples lie
Open unto the fields, and to the sky;
All bright and glittering in the smokeless air.
Never did sun more beautifully steep
In his first splendor, valley, rock, or hill;
Ne'er saw I, never felt, a calm so deep!
The river glideth at his own sweet will:

[80]

Dear God! the very houses seem asleep;
And all that mighty heart is lying still!

¶ A poet writes when he is most moved, because writing poems is very difficult and poets will not undertake the labor except when they have something they want very much to say. Many things can move us—indignation, love, fear—but again and again a poet is moved by the beauty of something he sees: like Wordsworth looking at London, or like Carew on Spring.

THE SPRING

Thomas Carew (1595?–1639?)

Now that the winter's gone, the earth hath lost
Her snow-white robes, and now no more the frost
Candies the grass, or casts an icy cream
Upon the silver Lake, or crystal stream:
But the warm Sun thaws the benumbèd Earth,
And makes it tender, gives a sacred birth
To the dead Swallow; wakes in hollow tree
The drowsy Cuckoo, and the Humble-Bee.
Now do a quire of chirping Minstrels bring
In triumph to the world, the youthful Spring.
The Valleys, hills, and woods, in rich array,
Welcome the coming of the longed-for May.
Now all things smile; only my Love doth lower:
Nor hath the scalding Noon-day-Sun the power,
To melt that marble ice, which still doth hold
Her heart congealed, and makes her pity cold.
The Ox which lately did for shelter fly

[81]

Into the stall, doth now securely lie
In open fields; and love no more is made
By the fire side; but in the cooler shade
Amyntas now doth with his Cloris sleep
Under a sycamore; and all things keep
Time with the season: only she doth carry
June in her eyes, in her heart January.

THE FUNERAL RITES OF THE ROSE

Robert Herrick (1591–1674)

The Rose was sick and smiling died;
And, being to be sanctified,
About the bed there sighing stood
The sweet and flowery sisterhood:
Some hung the head, while some did bring,
To wash her, water from the spring;
Some laid her forth, while others wept,
But all a solemn fast there kept:
The holy sisters, some among,
The sacred dirge and trental sung.
But ah! what sweets smelt everywhere,
As Heaven had spent all perfumes there.
At last, when prayers for the dead
And rites were all accomplishèd,
They, weeping, spread a lawny loom,
And closed her up as in a tomb.

"MY HEART LEAPS UP"

William Wordsworth (1770–1850)

ह∾ ∾ई

My heart leaps up when I behold
    A rainbow in the sky:
So was it when my life began;
So is it now I am a man;
So be it when I shall grow old,
    Or let me die!
The Child is father of the Man;
And I could wish my days to be
Bound each to each by natural piety.

THE SOLITARY REAPER

William Wordsworth (1770–1850)

ह∾ ∾ई

Behold her, single in the field,
Yon solitary Highland Lass!
Reaping and singing by herself;
Stop here, or gently pass!
Alone she cuts and binds the grain,
And sings a melancholy strain;
O listen! for the vale profound
Is overflowing with the sound.

No nightingale did ever chaunt
More welcome notes to weary bands
Of travelers in some shady haunt,
Among Arabian sands:

A voice so thrilling ne'er was heard
In spring-time from the cuckoo bird,
Breaking the silence of the seas
Among the farthest Hebrides.

Will no one tell me what she sings?
Perhaps the plaintive numbers flow
For old, unhappy, far-off things,
And battles long ago:
Or is it some more humble lay,
Familiar matter of today?
Some natural sorrow, loss or pain,
That has been, and may be again?

Whate'er the theme, the maiden sang
As if her song could have no ending;
I saw her singing at her work,
And o'er the sickle bending;
I listened, motionless and still;
And, as I mounted up the hill,
The music in my heart I bore,
Long after it was heard no more.

THE THRUSH'S NEST

John Clare (1793–1864)

ح‌‌ص

Within a thick and spreading hawthorn bush,
That overhung a molehill large and round,
I heard from morn to morn a merry thrush
Sing hymns to sunrise, and I drank the sound
With joy; and, often, an intruding guest,
I watched her secret toil from day to day—
How true she warped the moss, to form a nest,

[84]

And modelled it within with wood and clay;
And by and by, like heath-bells gilt with dew,
There lay her shining eggs, as bright as flowers,
Ink-spotted-over shells of greeny blue;
And there I witnessed, in the sunny hours
A brood of nature's minstrels chirp and fly,
Glad as the sunshine and the laughing sky.

TO AUTUMN

John Keats (1795–1821)

Season of mists and mellow fruitfulness
    Close bosom-friend of the maturing sun;
Conspiring with him how to load and bless
    With fruit the vines that round the thatch-eaves run;
To bend with apples the moss'd cottage-trees,
    And fill all fruit with ripeness to the core;
      To swell the gourd, and plump the hazel shells
With a sweet kernel; to set budding more,
And still more, later flowers for the bees,
Until they think warm days will never cease;
    For Summer has o'er-brimm'd their clammy cells.

Who hath not seen thee oft amid thy store?
    Sometimes whoever seeks abroad may find
Thee sitting careless on a granary floor,
    Thy hair soft-lifted by the winnowing wind;
Or on a half-reap'd furrow sound asleep,
    Drowsed with the fume of poppies, while thy hook
      Spares the next swath and all its twined flowers;
    And sometimes like a gleaner thou dost keep
Steady thy laden head across a brook;
Or by a cider-press, with patient look,
    Thou watchest the last oozings, hours by hours.

Where are the songs of Spring? Ay, where are they?
　　Think not of them, thou hast thy music too,—
While barred clouds bloom the soft-dying day
　　And touch the stubble-plains with rosy hue;
Then in a wailful choir the small gnats mourn
　　Among the river sallows, borne aloft
　　　　Or sinking as the light wind lives or dies;
　　And full-grown lambs loud bleat from hilly bourn;
Hedge-crickets sing; and now with treble soft
The red-breast whistles from a garden-croft;
　　And gathering swallows twitter in the skies.

"FARTHER IN SUMMER THAN THE BIRDS"

Emily Dickinson (1830–1886)

Farther in summer than the birds,
Pathetic from the grass,
A minor nation celebrates
Its unobtrusive mass.

No ordinance is seen,
So gradual the grace,
A pensive custom it becomes,
Enlarging loneliness.

Antiquest felt at noon
When August, burning low,
Calls forth this spectral canticle,
Repose to typify.

Remit as yet no grace,
No furrow on the glow,
Yet a druidic difference
Enhances nature now.

druidic: Druids were the priests of an ancient and mysterious religion.

"THERE'S A CERTAIN SLANT OF LIGHT"

Emily Dickinson (1830–1886)

There's a certain slant of light,
On winter afternoons,
That oppresses, like the weight
Of cathedral tunes.

Heavenly hurt it gives us;
We can find no scar,
But internal difference
Where the meanings are.

None may teach it anything,
'Tis the seal, despair,—
An imperial affliction
Sent us of the air.

When it comes, the landscape listens,
Shadows hold their breath;
When it goes, 'tis like the distance
On the look of death.

LONDON SNOW

Robert Bridges (1844–1930)

When men were all asleep the snow came flying,
In large white flakes falling on the city brown,
Stealthily and perpetually settling the loosely lying,
    Hushing the latest traffic of the drowsy town;

[87]

Deadening, muffling, stifling its murmurs failing;
Lazily and incessantly floating down and down:
    Silently sifting and veiling road, roof and railing;
Hiding difference, making unevenness even,
Into angles and crevices softly drifting and sailing.
    All night it fell, and when full inches seven
It lay in the depth of its uncompacted lightness,
The clouds blew off from a high and frosty heaven;
    And all woke earlier for the unaccustomed brightness
Of the winter dawning, the strange unheavenly glare:
The eye marveled—marveled at the dazzling whiteness;
    The ear hearkened to the stillness of the solemn air;
No sound of wheel rumbling nor of foot falling,
And the busy morning cries came thin and spare.
    Then boys I heard, as they went to school, calling;
They gathered up the crystal manna to freeze
Their tongues with tasting, their hands with snow-balling;
    Or rioted in a drift, plunging up to the knees;
Or peering up from under the white-mossed wonder,
"O look at the trees!" they cried, "O look at the trees!"
    With lessened load a few carts creak and blunder,
Following along the white deserted way,
A country company long dispersed asunder:
    When now already the sun, in pale display
Standing by Paul's high dome, spread forth below
His sparkling beams, and awoke the stir of day.
    For now doors open, and war is waged with the snow;
And trains of somber men, past tale of number,
Tread long brown paths, as toward their toil they go:
    But even for them awhile no cares encumber
Their minds diverted; the daily word is unspoken,
The daily thoughts of labor and sorrow slumber
At the sight of the beauty that greets them, for the charm they
        have broken.

[88]

THE DARK HILLS

Edwin Arlington Robinson (1869–1935)

ঌ৯ ৵৽

Dark hills at evening in the west,
Where sunset hovers like a sound
Of golden horns that sang to rest
Old bones of warriors under ground,
Far now from all the bannered ways
Where flash the legions of the sun,
You fade—as if the last of days
Were fading, and all wars were done.

THE SHEAVES

Edwin Arlington Robinson (1869–1935)

ঌ৯ ৵৽

Where long the shadows of the wind had rolled,
Green wheat was yielding to the change assigned;
And as by some vast magic undivined
The world was turning slowly into gold.
Like nothing that was ever bought or sold
It waited there, the body and the mind;
And with a mighty meaning of a kind
That tells the more the more it is not told.

So in a land where all days are not fair,
Fair days went on till on another day
A thousand golden sheaves were lying there,
Shining and still, but not for long to stay—
As if a thousand girls with golden hair
Might rise from where they slept and go away.

STOPPING BY WOODS ON
A SNOWY EVENING

Robert Frost (1875–   )

ক্ষ ক্ষ

Whose woods these are I think I know.
His house is in the village though;
He will not see me stopping here
To watch his woods fill up with snow.

My little horse must think it queer
To stop without a farmhouse near
Between the woods and frozen lake
The darkest evening of the year.

He gives his harness bells a shake
To ask if there is some mistake.
The only other sound's the sweep
Of easy wind and downy flake.

The woods are lovely, dark and deep,
But I have promises to keep,
And miles to go before I sleep,
And miles to go before I sleep.

THE NEED OF BEING VERSED
IN COUNTRY THINGS

Robert Frost (1875–   )

ক্ষ ক্ষ

The house had gone to bring again
To the midnight sky a sunset glow.
Now the chimney was all of the house that stood,
Like a pistil after the petals go.

The barn opposed across the way,
That would have joined the house in flame
Had it been the will of the wind, was left
To bear forsaken the place's name.

No more it opened with all one end
For teams that came by the stony road
To drum on the floor with scurrying hoofs
And brush the mow with the summer load.

The birds that came to it through the air
At broken windows flew out and in,
Their murmur more like the sigh we sigh
From too much dwelling on what has been.

Yet for them the lilac renewed its leaf,
And the aged elm, though touched with fire;
And the dry pump flung up an awkward arm;
And the fence post carried a strand of wire.

For them there was really nothing sad.
But though they rejoiced in the nest they kept,
One had to be versed in country things
Not to believe the phoebes wept.

MENDING WALL

Robert Frost (1875–)

Something there is that doesn't love a wall,
That sends the frozen-ground-swell under it,
And spills the upper boulders in the sun;
And makes gaps even two can pass abreast.
The work of hunters is another thing:
I have come after them and made repair

Where they have left not one stone on a stone,
But they would have the rabbit out of hiding,
To please the yelping dogs. The gaps I mean,
No one has seen them made or heard them made,
But at spring mending-time we find them there.
I let my neighbor know beyond the hill;
And on a day we meet to walk the line
And set the wall between us once again.
We keep the wall between us as we go.
To each the boulders that have fallen to each.
And some are loaves and some so nearly balls
We have to use a spell to make them balance:
"Stay where you are until our backs are turned!"
We wear our fingers rough with handling them.
Oh, just another kind of outdoor game,
One on a side. It comes to little more:
There where it is we do not need the wall:
He is all pine and I am apple orchard.
My apple trees will never get across
And eat the cones under his pines, I tell him.
He only says, "Good fences make good neighbors."
Spring is the mischief in me, and I wonder
If I could put a notion in his head:
"*Why* do they make good neighbors? Isn't it
Where there are cows? But here there are no cows.
Before I built a wall I'd ask to know
What I was walling in or walling out,
And to whom I was like to give offense.
Something there is that doesn't love a wall,
That wants it down." I could say "Elves" to him,
But it's not elves exactly, and I'd rather
He said it for himself. I see him there
Bringing a stone grasped firmly by the top
In each hand, like an old-stone savage armed.
He moves in darkness as it seems to me,
Not of woods only and the shade of trees.
He will not go behind his father's saying,
And he likes having thought of it so well
He says again, "Good fences make good neighbors."

BAVARIAN GENTIANS

D. H. Lawrence (1885–1930)

Not every man has gentians in his house
in soft September, at slow, sad Michaelmas.

Bavarian gentians, big and dark, only dark
darkening the day-time torch-like with the smoking blueness
    of Pluto's gloom,
ribbed and torch-like, with their blaze of darkness spread blue
down flattening into points, flattened under the sweep of white
    day
torch-flower of the blue-smoking darkness, Pluto's dark-blue
    daze,
black lamps from the halls of Dio, burning dark blue,
giving off darkness, blue darkness, as Demeter's pale lamps give
    off light,
lead me then, lead me the way.
Reach me a gentian, give me a torch!
let me guide myself with the blue, forked torch of this flower
down the darker and darker stairs, where blue is darkened on
    blueness,
even where Persephone goes, just now, from the frosted Sep-
    tember
to the sightless realm where darkness is awake upon the dark
and Persephone herself is but a voice
or a darkness invisible enfolded in the deeper dark
of the arms Plutonic, and pierced with the passion of dense
    gloom,
among the splendor of torches of darkness, shedding darkness
    on the lost bride and her groom.

NEW HAMPSHIRE

T. S. Eliot (1888–   )

Children's voices in the orchard
Between the blossom- and the fruit-time:
Golden head, crimson head,
Between the green tip and the root.
Black wing, brown wing, hover over;
Twenty years and the spring is over;
Today grieves, tomorrow grieves,
Cover me over, light-in-leaves;
Golden head, black wing,
Cling, swing,
Spring, sing,
Swing up into the apple-tree.

VIRGINIA

T. S. Eliot (1888–   )

Red river, red river,
Slow flow heat is silence
No will is still as a river
Still. Will heat move
Only through the mocking-bird
Heard once? Still hills
Wait. Gates wait. Purple trees,
White trees, wait, wait,
Delay, decay. Living, living,
Never moving. Ever moving
Iron thoughts came with me
And go with me:
Red river, river, river.

DAFFODILS

William Wordsworth (*1770–1850*)

I wandered lonely as a cloud
That floats on high o'er vales and hills,
When all at once I saw a crowd,
A host of golden daffodils,
Beside the lake, beneath the trees
Fluttering and dancing in the breeze.

Continuous as the stars that shine
And twinkle on the milky way,
They stretched in never-ending line
Along the margin of a bay:
Ten thousand saw I at a glance
Tossing their heads in sprightly dance.
The waves beside them danced, but they
Outdid the sparkling waves in glee:
A poet could not but be gay
In such a jocund company:
I gazed—and gazed—but little thought
What wealth the show to me had brought:

For oft, when on my couch I lie
In vacant or in pensive mood,
They flash upon that inward eye
Which is the bliss of solitude;
And then my heart with pleasure fills,
And dances with the daffodils.

¶ Wordsworth takes nature largely for what it is. Many poets use natural things as symbols of human things.

ODE TO THE WEST WIND

Percy Bysshe Shelley (1792–1822)

ॐ

I

O Wild West Wind, thou breath of Autumn's being,
Thou, from whose unseen presence the leaves dead
Are driven, like ghosts from an enchanter fleeing,

Yellow, and black, and pale, and hectic red,
Pestilence-stricken multitudes: O thou,
Who chariotest to their dark wintry bed

The winged seeds, where they lie cold and low,
Each like a corpse within its grave, until
Thine azure sister of the Spring shall blow

Her clarion o'er the dreaming earth, and fill
(Driving sweet buds like flocks to feed in air)
With living hues and odors plain and hill:

Wild Spirit, which art moving everywhere;
Destroyer and preserver; hear, oh, hear!

II

Thou on whose stream, mid the steep sky's commotion,
Loose clouds like earth's decaying leaves are shed,
Shook from the tangled boughs of Heaven and Ocean,

Angels of rain and lightning: there are spread
On the blue surface of thine airy surge,
Like the bright hair uplifted from the head

Of some fierce Maenad, even from the dim verge
Of the horizon to the zenith's height,
The locks of the approaching storm. Thou dirge

Of the dying year, to which this closing night
Will be the dome of a vast sepulchre,
Vaulted with all thy congregated might

Of vapors, from whose solid atmosphere
Black rain, and fire, and hail will burst: oh, hear!

III

Thou who didst waken from his summer dreams
The blue Mediterranean, where he lay,
Lulled by the coil of his crystàlline streams,

Beside a pumice isle in Baiae's bay,
And saw in sleep old palaces and towers
Quivering within the wave's intenser day,

All overgrown with azure moss and flowers
So sweet, the sense faints picturing them! Thou
For whose path the Atlantic's level powers

Cleave themselves into chasms, while far below
The sea-blooms and the oozy woods which wear
The sapless foliage of the ocean, know

Thy voice, and suddenly grow gray with fear,
And tremble and despoil themselves: oh, hear!

IV

If I were a dead leaf thou mightest bear;
If I were a swift cloud to fly with thee;
A wave to pant beneath thy power, and share

The impulse of thy strength, only less free
Than thou, O uncontrollable! If even
I were as in my boyhood, and could be

The comrade of thy wanderings over Heaven,
As then, when to outstrip thy skyey speed
Scarce seemed a vision; I would ne'er have striven

As thus with thee in prayer in my sore need.
Oh, lift me as a wave, a leaf, a cloud!
I fall upon the thorns of life! I bleed!

A heavy weight of hours has chained and bowed
One too like thee: tameless, and swift, and proud.

Make me thy lyre, even as the forest is:
What if my leaves are falling like its own!
The tumult of thy mighty harmonies

Will take from both a deep, autumnal tone,
Sweet though in sadness. Be thou, Spirit fierce,
My spirit! Be thou me, impetuous one!

Drive my dead thoughts over the universe
Like withered leaves to quicken a new birth!
And, by the incantation of this verse,

Scatter, as from an unextinguished hearth
Ashes and sparks, my words among mankind!
Be through my lips to unawakened earth

The trumpet of a prophecy! O, Wind,
If Winter comes, can Spring be far behind?

AUTUMNAL SPRING SONG

Vassar Miller (1924–)

When autumn wounds the bough
And bleeds me white and shaken,
Forbear to tell me how
The spring must reawaken
 And the trees bloom on forever,
 But with the same leaves never.

When autumn smears the sheen
Of leaf-lace, nature's lore
Affirms each season's green
To shimmer as before
 While the trees bloom on forever.
 But with the same leaves? Never.

When every branch is whole
The bitter sword of spring
Will scar the forest's soul
And mine remembering
 That the trees bloom on forever,
 But with the same leaves never.

Lord, You must comfort me
When woods are autumn's spoil,
Yet with another Tree
Unnourished by the soil
 Whence the trees bloom on forever,
 But with the same leaves never.

AUGUST HAIL

J. V. Cunningham (1911–)

In late summer the wild geese
In the white draws are flying.
The grain beards in the blue peace.
The weeds are drying.

The hushed sky breeds hail.
Who shall revenge unreason?
Wheat headless in the white flail
Denies the season.

¶ Animals are part of the nature which poets describe.
Here are some more skeltonics.

VENGENCE ON CATS

John Skelton (1460?–1529)

That vengence I ask and cry,
By way of exclamation,
On all the whole cat nation
Of cattes wild and tame:
God send them sorrow and shame!
That cat specially
That slew so cruelly
My little pretty sparrow

That I brought up at Carow.
     O cat of carlish kind,
The fiend was in thy mind
When thou my bird untwined!
I would thou haddest been blind!
The leopardes savage,
The lions in their rage,
Might catch thee in their paws,
And gnaw thee in their jaws!
The serpentes of Lybany
Might sting thee venimously!
The dragons with their tongues
Might poison thy liver and lungs!
The manticors of the mountains
Might feed them on thy brains! . . .
     Of Inde the greedy gripes
Might tear out all thy tripes!
Of Arcady the bears
Might pluck away thine ears!
The wild wolf Lycaon
Bite asunder thy back bone!
Of Ethna the burning hill,
That day and night burneth still,
Set in thy tail a blaze,
That all the world may gaze
And wonder upon thee,
From Ocean the great sea
Unto the Isles of Orchady,
From Tillbery ferry
To the plain of Salisbery!
So traitorously my bird to kill
That never ought thee evil will! . . .

cattes: cats   *carlish:* churlish

SNAKE

D. H. Lawrence (1885–1930)

A snake came to my water-trough
On a hot, hot day, and I in pajamas for the heat,
To drink there.

In the deep, strange-scented shade of the great dark carob-tree
I came down the steps with my pitcher
And must wait, must stand and wait, for there he was at the
trough before me.

He reached down from a fissure in the earth-wall in the gloom
And trailed his yellow-brown slackness soft-bellied down,
over the edge of the stone trough

And rested his throat upon the stone bottom,
And where the water had dripped from the tap, in a small
clearness,
He sipped with his straight mouth,
Softly drinking through his straight gums, into his slack long
body,
Silently.

Someone was before me at my water-trough,
And I, like a second comer, waiting.

He lifted his head from his drinking, as cattle do,
And looked at me vaguely, as drinking cattle do,
And flickered his two-forked tongue from his lips, and mused
a moment,
And stooped and drank a little more,
Being earth-brown, earth-golden from the burning bowels of
the earth
On the day of Sicilian July, with Etna smoking.

The voice of my education said to me
He must be killed,
For in Sicily the black, black snakes are innocent, the gold are
venomous.

And voices in me said, If you were a man
You would take a stick and break him now, and finish him off.

But must I confess how I liked him,
How glad I was he had come like a guest in quiet, to drink at
my water-trough
And depart peaceful, pacified, and thankless,
Into the burning bowels of this earth?

Was it cowardice, that I dared not kill him?
Was it perversity, that I longed to talk to him?
Was it humility, to feel so honored?
I felt so honored.

And yet those voices:
If you were not afraid, you would kill him!

And truly I was afraid, I was most afraid,
But even so, honored still more
That he should seek my hospitality
From out the dark door of the secret earth.

He drank enough
And lifted his head, dreamily, as one who has drunken,
And flickered his tongue like a forked night on the air, so
black,
Seeming to lick his lips,
And looked around like a god, unseeing, into the air,
And slowly turned his head,
And slowly, very slowly, as if thrice adream,
Proceeded to draw his slow length curving round
And climb again the broken bank of my wall-face.
And as he put his head into that dreadful hole,

[103]

And as he slowly drew up, snake-easing his shoulders, and
                                            entered farther,
A sort of horror, a sort of protest against his withdrawing into
                                            that horrid black hole,
Deliberately going into the blackness, and slowly drawing
                                            himself after,
Overcame me now his back was turned.

I looked round, I put down my pitcher,
I picked up a clumsy log,
And threw it at the water-trough with a clatter.

I think it did not hit him,
But suddenly that part of him that was left behind convulsed
                                            in undignified haste,
Writhed like lightning, and was gone
Into the black hole, the earth-lipped fissure in the wall-front,
At which, in the intense still noon, I stared with fascination.

And immediately I regretted it.
I thought how paltry, how vulgar, what a mean act!
I despised myself and the voices of my accursed human edu-
                                            cation.

And I thought of the albatross,
And I wished he would come back, my snake.

For he seemed to me again like a king,
Like a king in exile, uncrowned in the underworld,
Now due to be crowned again.

And so, I missed my chance with one of the lords
Of life.
And I have something to expiate;
A pettiness.

PROUD SONGSTERS

Thomas Hardy (1840–1928)

રેટ એ

The thrushes sing as the sun is going,
And the finches whistle in ones and pairs,
And as it gets dark loud nightingales
  In bushes
Pipe, as they can when April wears,
 As if all Time were theirs.
These are brand-new birds of twelve-months' growing,
Which a year ago, or less than twain,
No finches were, nor nightingales,
  Nor thrushes,
But only particles of grain,
 And earth, and air, and rain.

THE OWL

Edward Thomas (1887–1917)

રેટ એ

Downhill I came, hungry, and yet not starved;
Cold, yet had heat within me that was proof
Against the North wind; tired, yet so that rest
Had seemed the sweetest thing under a roof.

Then at the inn I had food, fire, and rest,
Knowing how hungry, cold, and tired was I.
All of the night quite barred out except
An owl's cry, a most melancholy cry

Shaken out long and clear upon the hill,
No merry note, nor cause of merriment,

But one telling me plain what I escaped
And others could not, that night, as in I went.

And salted was my food, and my repose,
Salted and sobered, too, by the bird's voice
Speaking for all who lay under the stars,
Soldiers and poor, unable to rejoice.

THE DARKLING THRUSH

Thomas Hardy (1840–1928)

I leant upon a coppice gate
    When Frost was specter-gray,
And Winter's dregs made desolate
    The weakening eye of day.
The tangled bine-stems scored the sky
    Like strings from broken lyres,
And all mankind that haunted nigh
    Had sought their household fires.

The land's sharp features seemed to be
    The Century's corpse outleant;
His crypt the cloudy canopy,
    The wind his death-lament.
The ancient pulse of germ and birth
    Was shrunken hard and dry,
And every spirit upon earth
    Seemed fervorless as I.

At once a voice arose among
    The bleak twigs overhead
In a full-hearted evensong
    Of joy illimited;

An aged thrush, frail, gaunt and small,
    In blast-beruffled plume,
Had chosen thus to fling his soul
    Upon the growing gloom.

So little cause for carolings
    Of such ecstatic sound
Was written on terrestrial things
    Afar or nigh around,
That I could think there trembled through
    His happy good-night air
Some blessed hope, whereof he knew
    And I was unaware.

"A NOISELESS PATIENT SPIDER"

Walt Whitman (1819–1892)

෨෯ ෯෨

A noiseless patient spider,
I mark'd where on a little promontory it stood isolated,
Mark'd how to explore the vacant vast surrounding,
It launch'd forth filament, filament, filament, out of itself.
Ever unreeling down, ever tirelessly speeding them.
And you O my soul where you stand,
Surrounded, detached, in measureless oceans of space,
Ceaselessly musing, venturing, throwing, seeking the spheres
    to connect them,
Till the bridge you will need be form'd, till the ductile anchor
    hold,
Till the gossamer thread you fling catch somewhere, O my
    soul.

¶ Poets use animals as symbols, too.

"LIKE AS A HUNTSMAN"

Edmund Spenser (1552?–1599)

෩෩෩

Like as a huntsman after weary chase,
Seeing the game from him escaped away,
Sits down to rest him in some shady place,
With panting hounds, beguilèd of their prey:
So after long pursuit and vain assay,
When I all weary had the chase forsook,
The gentle deer return'd the self-same way,
Thinking to quench her thirst at the next brook.
There she, beholding me with milder look,
Sought not to fly, but fearless still did bide:
Till I in hand her yet half trembling took,
And with her own good-will her firmly tied.
    Strange thing, me seemed, to see a beast so wild
    So goodly won, with her own will beguiled.

THE WHALE

John Donne (1573–1631)

෩෩෩

At every stroke his brazen fins do take,
More circles in the broken sea they make
Than cannons' voices, when the air they tear.
His ribs are pillars, and his high arch'd roof
Of bark that blunts best steel, is thunder-proof.
Swim in him swallow'd dolphins, without fear,
And feel no sides, as if his vast womb were
Some inland sea, and ever as he went

He spouted rivers up, as if he meant
    To join our seas with seas above the firmament.

He hunts not fish, but as an officer,
Stays in his court, at his own net, and there
All suitors of all sorts themselves enthrall;
So on his back lies this whale wantoning,
And in his gulf-like throat sucks every thing
That passeth near. Fish chaseth fish, and all,
Flyer and follower, in this whirlpool fall;
O might not states of more equality
Consist? and is it of necessity
    That thousand guiltless smalls, to make one great, must
      die?

THE BELLS OF HEAVEN

Ralph Hodgson (*1871–*)

'Twould ring the bells of Heaven
The wildest peal for years,
If Parson lost his senses
And people came to theirs,
And he and they together
Knelt down with angry prayers
For tamed and shabby tigers,
And dancing dogs and bears,
And wretched, blind pit-ponies,
And little hunted hares.

AN ELEGY ON THE DEATH OF A MAD DOG

Oliver Goldsmith (1730–1774)

ফ৹ ৎ৶

Good people all, of every sort,
    Give ear unto my song;
And if you find it wondrous short,
    It cannot hold you long.

In Islington there was a man,
    Of whom the world might say,
That still a godly race he ran,
    Whene'er he went to pray.

A kind and gentle heart he had,
    To comfort friends and foes;
And naked every day he clad,
    When he put on his clothes.

And in that town a dog was found,
    As many dogs there be,
Both mongrel, puppy, whelp, and hound,
    And curs of low degree.

This dog and man at first were friends;
    But when a pique began,
The dog, to gain his private ends,
    Went mad, and bit the man.

Around from all the neighboring streets
    The wondering neighbors ran,
And swore the dog had lost his wits,
    To bite so good a man.

The wound it seem'd both sore and sad
    To every Christian eye;
And while they swore the dog was mad,
    They swore the man would die.

But soon a wonder came to light,
    That show'd the rogues they lied:
The man recover'd of the bite,
    The dog it was that died.

¶ The next poem was written in a mad house, which does not prevent it from being magnificent—even if you don't admire cats.

MY CAT JEOFFRY

Christopher Smart (1722–1770)

For I will consider my Cat Jeoffry.

For he is the servant of the Living God, duly and daily serving him.

For at the First glance of the glory of God in the East he worships in his way.

For is this done by wreathing his body seven times round with elegant quickness.

For then he leaps up to catch the musk, which is the blessing of God upon his prayer.

For he rolls upon prank to work it in.

For having done duty and received blessing he begins to consider himself.

For this he performs in ten degrees.

For First he looks upon his fore-paws to see if they are clean.

For Secondly he kicks up behind to clear away there.

For Thirdly he works it upon stretch with the fore-paws extended.

For Fourthly he sharpens his paws by wood.

For Fifthly he washes himself.

For Sixthly he rolls upon wash.

For Seventhly he fleas himself, that he may not be interrupted upon the beat.

For Eighthly he rubs himself against a post.

For Ninthly he looks up for his instructions.

For Tenthly he goes in quest of food.

For having consider'd God and himself he will consider his neighbor.

For if he meets another cat he will kiss her in kindness.

For when he takes his prey he plays with it to give it a chance.

For one mouse in seven escapes by his dallying.

For when his day's work is done his business more properly begins.

For he keeps the Lord's watch in the night against the adversary.

For he counteracts the powers of darkness by his electrical skin and glaring eyes.

For he counteracts the Devil, who is death, by brisking about the life.

For in his morning orisons he loves the sun and the sun loves him.

For he is of the tribe of Tiger.

For the Cherub Cat is a term of the Angel Tiger.

For he has the subtlety and hissing of a serpent, which in goodness he suppresses.

For he will not do destruction, if he is well fed, neither will he spit without provocation.

For he purrs in thankfulness, when God tells him he's a good Cat.

For he is an instrument for the children to learn benevolence upon.

For every house is incomplete without him and a blessing is lacking in the spirit.

For the Lord commanded Moses concerning the cats at the departure of the Children of Israel from Egypt.

For every family had one cat at least in the bag.

For the English Cats are the best in Europe.

For he is the cleanest in the use of his fore-paws of any quad-
 rupede.

For the dexterity of his defense is an instance of the love of
 God to him exceedingly.

For he is the quickest to his mark of any creature.

For he is tenacious of his point.

For he is a mixture of gravity and waggery.

For he knows that God is his Savior.

For there is nothing sweeter than his peace when at rest.

For there is nothing brisker than his life when in motion.

For he is of the Lord's poor and so indeed is he called by
 benevolence perpetually—Poor Jeoffry! poor Jeoffry! the
 rat has bit thy throat.

For I bless the name of the Lord Jesus that Jeoffry is better.

For the divine spirit comes about his body to sustain it in complete cat.

For his tongue is exceedingly pure so that it has in purity what
 it wants in music.

For he is docile and can learn certain things.

For he can set up with gravity which is patience upon appro-
 bation.

For he can fetch and carry, which is patience in employment.

For he can jump over a stick which is patience upon proof
 positive.

For he can spraggle upon waggle at the word of command.

For he can jump from an eminence into his master's bosom.

For he can catch the cork and toss it again.

For he is hated by the hypocrite and miser.

For the former is afraid of detection.

For the latter refuses the charge.

For he camels his back to bear the first notion of business.

For he is good to think on, if a man would express himself
 neatly.

For he made a great figure in Egypt for his signal services.

For he killed the Icneumon-rat very pernicious by land.

For his ears are so acute that they sting again.

For from this proceeds the passing quickness of his attention.

For by stroking of him I have found out electricity.

[113]

For I perceived God's light about him both wax and fire.
For the Electrical fire is the spiritual substance, which God
    sends from heaven to sustain the bodies both of man and
    beast.
For God has blessed him in the variety of his movements.
For, tho he cannot fly, he is an excellent clamberer.
For his motions upon the face of the earth are more than any
    other quadrupede.
For he can tread to all the measures upon the music.
For he can swim for life.
For he can creep.

CAT ON COUCH

Barbara Howes (1914–   )

꧁꧂

My cat, washing her tail's tip, is a whorl
Of white shell,
As perfect as a fan
In full half-moon . . . Next moment she's a hare:
The muzzle softens, rounds, goes dumb, and one
Tall ear dips, falters forward . . . Then,
Cross as switches, she's a great horned owl;
Two leafy tricorned ears reverse, a frown
Darkens her chalky visage, big eyes round
And round and stare down midnight. There sits my cat

Mysterious as gauze,—now somnolent,
Now jocose, quicksilver from a dropped
Thermometer. When poised
Below the sketched ballet-
Dancers who pirouette upon the wall,
Calmly she lifts the slim
Boom of her leg, what will

[114]

The prima ballerina next
Perform?—Grace held in readiness,
She meditates, a vision of repose.

THE FLY

William Blake (1757–1827)

ह‌~ ~ॐ

Little Fly,
Thy summer's play
My thoughtless hand
Has brushed away.

Am not I
A fly like thee?
Or art not thou
A man like me?

For I dance
And drink, and sing,
Till some blind hand
Shall brush my wing.

If thought is life
And strength and breath,
And the want
Of thought is death,

Then am I
A happy fly
If I live
Or if I die.

THE TIGER

William Blake (1757–1827)

Tiger! Tiger! burning bright
In the forests of the night,
What immortal hand or eye
Could frame thy fearful symmetry?

In what distant deeps or skies
Burnt the fire of thine eyes?
On what wings dare he aspire?
What the hand dare seize the fire?

And what shoulder, and what art,
Could twist the sinews of thy heart?
And when thy heart began to beat,
What dread hand? and what dread feet?

What the hammer? What the chain?
In what furnace was thy brain?
What the anvil? what dread grasp
Dare its deadly terrors clasp?

When the stars threw down their spears,
And water'd heaven with their tears,
Did He smile his work to see?
Did He who made the Lamb make thee?

Tiger! Tiger! burning bright
In the forests of the night,
What immortal hand or eye,
Dare frame thy fearful symmetry?

THE OXEN

Thomas Hardy (1840–1928)

Christmas Eve, and twelve of the clock.
 "Now they are all on their knees,"
An elder said as we sat in a flock
 By the embers in hearthside ease.

We pictured the meek mild creatures where
 They dwelt in their strawy pen,
Nor did it occur to one of us there
 To doubt they were kneeling then.

So fair a fancy few would weave
 In these years! Yet, I feel,
If someone said on Christmas Eve,
 "Come; see the oxen kneel

"In the lonely barton by yonder coomb
 Our childhood used to know,"
I should go with him in the gloom,
 Hoping it might be so.

THE HORSES

Edwin Muir (1887–1959)

Barely a twelvemonth after
The seven days war that put the world to sleep,
Late in the evening the strange horses came.

barton: farm yard *coomb:* hollow on the flank of a hill

By then we had made our covenant with silence,
But in the first few days it was so still
We listened to our breathing and were afraid.
On the second day
The radios failed; we turned the knobs; no answer.
On the third day a warship passed us, heading north,
Dead bodies piled on the deck. On the sixth day
A plane plunged over us into the sea. Thereafter
Nothing. The radios dumb;
And still they stand in corners of our kitchens,
And stand, perhaps, turned on, in a million rooms
All over the world. But now if they should speak,
If on a sudden they should speak again,
If on the stroke of noon a voice should speak,
We would not listen, we would not let it bring
That old bad world that swallowed its children quick
At one great gulp. We would not have it again.
Sometimes we think of the nations lying asleep,
Curled blindly in impenetrable sorrow,
And then the thought confounds us with its strangeness.
The tractors lie about our fields; at evening
They look like dank sea-monsters couched and waiting.
We leave them where they are and let them rust:
"They'll moulder away and be like other loam."
We make our oxen drag our rusty ploughs,
Long laid aside. We have gone back
Far past our fathers' land.
                              And then, that evening
Late in the summer the strange horses came.
We heard a distant tapping on the road,
A deepening drumming; it stopped, went on again
And at the corner changed to hollow thunder.
We saw the heads
Like a wild wave charging and were afraid.
We had sold our horses in our fathers' time
To buy new tractors. Now they were strange to us
As fabulous steeds set on an ancient shield
Or illustrations in a book of knights.
We did not dare go near them. Yet they waited,

Stubborn and shy, as if they had been sent
By an old command to find our whereabouts
And that long-lost archaic companionship.
In the first moment we had never a thought
That they were creatures to be owned and used.
Among them were some half-a-dozen colts
Dropped in some wilderness of the broken world,
Yet new as if they had come from their own Eden.
Since then they have pulled our ploughs and borne our loads.
But that free servitude still can pierce our hearts.
Our life is changed; their coming our beginning.

¶ T. S. Eliot wrote "The Hippopotamus" before he joined the Church of England. The poem contrasts the church in the world—which remains very much a worldly institution—with the lowly parishioners who can attain paradise. Still, it is most charming for its imaginative picture, doctrine aside, of the hippo decked out as an angel.

THE HIPPOPOTAMUS

T. S. Eliot (1888–)

᭞᪶ ᪶᭞

*And when this epistle is read among you, cause
that it be read also in the church of the Laodiceans.*

The broad-backed hippopotamus
Rests on his belly in the mud;
Although he seems so firm to us
He is merely flesh and blood.

Flesh and blood is weak and frail,
Susceptible to nervous shock;

[119]

While the True Church can never fail
For it is based upon a rock.

The hippo's feeble steps may err
In compassing material ends,
While the True Church need never stir
To gather in its dividends.

The 'potamus can never reach
The mango on the mango-tree;
But fruits of pomegranate and peach
Refresh the Church from over sea.

At mating time the hippo's voice
Betrays inflexions hoarse and odd,
But every week we hear rejoice
The Church, at being one with God.

The hippopotamus's day
Is passed in sleep; at night he hunts;
God works in a mysterious way—
The Church can sleep and feed at once.

I saw the 'potamus take wing
Ascending from the damp savannas,
And quiring angels round him sing
The praise of God, in loud hosannas.

Blood of the Lamb shall wash him clean
And him shall heavenly arms enfold,
Among the saints he shall be seen
Performing on a harp of gold

He shall be washed as white as snow,
By all the martyr'd virgins kist,
While the True Church remains below
Wrapt in the old miasmal mist.

THE GROUNDHOG

Richard Eberhart (1904–   )

ॐ ॐ

In June, amid the golden fields,
I saw a groundhog lying dead.
Dead lay he; my senses shook,
And mind outshot our naked frailty.
There lowly in the vigorous summer
His form began its senseless change,
And made my senses waver dim
Seeing nature ferocious in him.
Inspecting close his maggots' might
And seething cauldron of his being,
Half with loathing, half with a strange love,
I poked him with an angry stick.
The fever arose, became a flame
And Vigour circumscribed the skies,
Immense energy in the sun,
And through my frame a sunless trembling.
My stick had done nor good nor harm.
Then stood I silent in the day
Watching the object, as before;
And kept my reverence for knowledge
Trying for control, to be still,
To quell the passion of the blood;
Until I had bent down on my knees
Praying for joy in the sight of decay.
And so I left; and I returned
In Autumn strict of eye, to see
The sap gone out of the groundhog,
But the bony sodden hulk remained.
But the year had lost its meaning,
And in intellectual chains
I lost both love and loathing,

Mured up in the wall of wisdom.
Another summer took the fields again
Massive and burning, full of life,
But when I chanced upon the spot
There was only a little hair left,
And bones bleaching in the sunlight
Beautiful as architecture;
I watched them like a geometer,
And cut a walking stick from a birch.
It has been three years, now.
There is no sign of the groundhog.
I stood there in the whirling summer,
My hand capped a withered heart,
And thought of China and of Greece,
Of Alexander in his tent;
Of Montaigne in his tower,
Of Saint Theresa in her wild lament.

¶ Death is probably the greatest single subject of the poet.
A groundhog is the source of one poem. Another may
start from a war. Ezra Pound wrote these lines about
World War I.

"THESE FOUGHT"

Ezra Pound (1885–   )

These fought in any case,
and some believing,

                              pro domo, in any case . . .

pro domo: for the home

Some quick to arm,
some for adventure,
some from fear of weakness,
some from fear of censure,
some for love of slaughter, in imagination,
learning later . . .
some in fear, learning love of slaughter;

Died some, pro patria,

                    non "dulce" non "et decor" . . .
walked eye-deep in hell
believing in old men's lies, then unbelieving
came home, home to a lie,
home to many deceits,
home to old lies and new infamy;
usury age-old and age-thick
and liars in public places.

Daring as never before, wastage as never before.
Young blood and high blood,
fair cheeks, and fine bodies;

fortitude as never before

frankness as never before,
disillusions as never told in the old days,
hysterias, trench confessions,
laughter out of dead bellies.

*   *   *   *

There died a myriad,
And of the best, among them,

pro patria: for the country
non "dulce" non "et decor": not "sweet" not "and proper" (Ezra Pound
    is answering the Roman poet Horace, who said it was "dulce et
    decor" to die "pro patria.")

[123]

For an old bitch gone in the teeth,
For a botched civilization,

Charm, smiling at the good mouth,
Quick eyes gone under earth's lid,
For two gross of broken statues,
For a few thousand battered books.

¶ The next poem came out of World War II.

TYWATER

Richard Wilbur (1921–   )

જ્જી જ્જી

Death of Sir Nihil, book the *nth*,
Upon the charred and clotted sward,
Lacking the lily of our Lord,
Alases of the hyacinth.

Could flicker from behind his ear
A whistling silver throwing knife,
And with a holler punch the life
Out of a swallow in the air.

Behind the lariat's butterfly
Shuttled his white and gritted grin,
And cuts of sky would roll within
The noose-hole, when he spun it high.

The violent, neat and practiced skill
Was all he loved and all he learned;
When he was hit, his body turned
To clumsy dirt before it fell.

[124]

And what to say of him, God knows.
Such violence. And such repose.

¶ Tywater was a soldier who had worked in a rodeo in
civilian life. Robert Lowell writes about the death of his
grandfather.

DEATH FROM CANCER
Robert Lowell (1917–)

ဇာ ဧ

This Easter, Arthur Winslow, less than dead,
Your people set you up in Phillips' House
To settle off your wrestling with the crab—
The claws drop flesh upon your yachting blouse
Until longshoreman Charon come and stab
Through your adjusted bed
And crush the crab. On Boston Basin, shells
Hit water by the Union Boat Club wharf:
You ponder why the coxes' squeakings dwarf
The *resurrexit dominus* of all the bells.
Grandfather Winslow, look, the swanboats coast
That island in the Public Gardens, where
The bread-stuffed ducks are brooding, where with tub
And strainer the mid-Sunday Irish scare
The sun-struck shallows for the dusky chub
This Easter, and the ghost
Of risen Jesus walks the waves to run
Arthur upon a trumpeting black swan
Beyond Charles River to the Acheron
Where the wide waters and their voyager are one.

¶ Dylan Thomas writes to his father.

[125]

"DO NOT GO GENTLE INTO THAT GOOD NIGHT"

Dylan Thomas (1914–1953)

Do not go gentle into that good night,
Old age should burn and rave at close of day;
Rage, rage against the dying of the light.

Though wise men at their end know dark is right,
Because their words had forked no lightning they
Do not go gentle into that good night.

Good men, the last wave by, crying how bright
Their frail deeds might have danced in a green bay,
Rage, rage against the dying of the light.

Wild men who caught and sang the sun in flight,
And learn, too late, they grieved it on its way,
Do not go gentle into that good night.

Grave men, near death, who see with blinding sight
Blind eyes could blaze like meteors and be gay,
Rage, rage against the dying of the light.

And you, my father, there on the sad height,
Curse, bless, me now with your fierce tears, I pray.
Do not go gentle into that good night.
Rage, rage against the dying of the light.

¶ W. E. Henley's title means, "In memory of sister Margaret."

I. M. MARGARITAE SORORI

W. E. Henley (1849–1903)

A late lark twitters from the quiet skies;
And from the west,
Where the sun, his day's work ended,
Lingers as in content,
There falls on the old, gray city
An influence luminous and serene,
A shining peace.

The smoke ascends
In a rosy-and-golden haze. The spires
Shine, and are changed. In the valley
Shadows rise. The lark sings on. The sun,
Closing his benediction,
Sinks, and the darkening air
Thrills with a sense of the triumphing night—
Night with her train of stars
And her great gift of sleep.

So be my passing!
My task accomplished and the long day done,
My wages taken, and in my heart
Some late lark singing,
Let me be gathered to the quiet west,
The sundown splendid and serene,
Death.

REQUIESCAT

Matthew Arnold (1822–1888)

Strew on her roses, roses,
    And never a spray of yew!
In quiet she reposes:
    Ah, would that I did too!

Her mirth the world required;
    She bathed it in smiles of glee.
But her heart was tired, tired,
    And now they let her be.

Her life was turning, turning,
    In mazes of heat and sound.
But for peace her soul was yearning,
    And now peace laps her round.

Her cabined, ample spirit,
    It fluttered and failed for breath.
Tonight it doth inherit
    The vasty hall of death.

HIDE-AND-SEEK

Robert Francis (1901–   )

Here where the dead lie hidden
Too well ever to speak,
Three children unforbidden
Are playing hide-and-seek.

What if for such a hiding
These stones were not designed?
The dead are far from chiding;
The living need not mind.

Too soon the stones that hid them
Anonymously in play
Will learn their names and bid them
Come back to hide to stay.

"WHEN I HAVE FEARS THAT I MAY CEASE TO BE"

John Keats (1795–1821)

ʒ❧ ❧ʒ

When I have fears that I may cease to be
    Before my pen has gleaned my teeming brain,
Before high-piled books, in charactery,
    Hold like rich garners the full ripened grain;
When I behold, upon the night's starred face,
    Huge cloudy symbols of a high romance,
And think that I may never live to trace
    Their shadows, with the magic hand of chance;
And when I feel, fair creature of an hour,
    That I shall never look upon thee more,
Never have relish in the faery power
    Of unreflecting love;—then on the shore
Of the wide world I stand alone, and think
Till love and fame to nothingness do sink.

¶ Keats knew that he was dying of tuberculosis. It was Shelley who wrote the great elegy on Keats's death.

From ADONAIS

Percy Bysshe Shelley (1792–1822)

. . .

He has outsoared the shadow of our night;
Envy and calumny and hate and pain,
And that unrest which men miscall delight,
Can touch him not and torture not again;
From the contagion of the world's slow stain
He is secure, and now can never mourn
A heart grown cold, a head grown gray in vain;
Nor, when the spirit's self has ceased to burn,
With sparkless ashes load an unlamented urn.

He lives, he wakes—'tis Death is dead, not he;
Mourn not for Adonais. —Thou young Dawn,
Turn all thy dew to splendor, for from thee
The spirit thou lamentest is not gone;
Ye caverns and ye forests, cease to moan!
Cease, ye faint flowers and fountains, and thou Air,
Which like a mourning veil thy scarf hadst thrown
O'er the abandoned Earth, now leave it bare
Even to the joyous stars which smile on its despair!

He is made one with Nature: there is heard
His voice in all her music, from the moan
Of thunder, to the song of night's sweet bird;
He is a presence to be felt and known
In darkness and in light, from herb and stone,
Spreading itself where'er that Power may move
Which has withdrawn his being to its own;
Which wields the world with never-wearied love,
Sustains it from beneath, and kindles it above.

[130]

He is a portion of the loveliness
Which once he made more lovely: he doth bear
His part, while the one Spirit's plastic stress
Sweeps through the dull dense world, compelling there,
All new successions to the forms they wear;
Torturing th' unwilling dross that checks its flight
To its own likeness, as each mass may bear;
And bursting in its beauty and its might
From trees and beasts and men into the Heaven's light . . .

AN EPITAPH ON SALATHIEL PAVY

Ben Jonson (1573–1637)

૭≈ ≈૭

Weep with me, all you that read
    This little story:
And know, for whom a tear you shed
    Death's self is sorry.
'T was a child that so did thrive
    In grace and feature,
As heaven and nature seemed to strive
    Which own'd the creature.
Years he numbered scarce thirteen
    When Fates turned cruel,
Yet three filled zodiacs had he been
    The stage's jewel;
And did act, what now we moan,
    Old men so duly,
As, sooth, the Parcae thought him one,
    He played so truly.
So, by error, to his fate
    They all consented;

three filled zodiacs: three years   *Parcae:* fates

[131]

But viewing him since, alas too late,
    They have repented,
And have sought, to give new birth,
    In baths to steep him;
But being so much too good for Earth,
    Heaven vows to keep him.

¶ Ben Jonson wrote about the untimely death of a boy
actor. Chidiock Tichbourne, sentenced to execution for
his part in a plot against Queen Elizabeth, wrote of the
untimely shortening of his life. He was not yet thirty.

ELEGY

Chidiock Tichbourne (1558–1586)

§

My prime of youth is but a frost of cares,
    My feast of joy is but a dish of pain,
My crop of corn is but a field of tares,
    And all my good is but vain hope of gain;
        The day is past, and yet I saw no sun,
        And now I live, and now my life is done.

My tale was heard and yet it was not told,
    My fruit is fallen and yet my leaves are green,
My youth is spent and yet I am not old,
    I saw the world and yet I was not seen;
        My thread is cut and yet it is not spun,
        And now I live, and now my life is done.

I sought my death and found it in my womb,
    I looked for life and saw it was a shade,

[132]

I trod the earth and knew it was my tomb,
　　And now I die, and now I was but made;
　　　My glass is full, and now my glass is run.
　　And now I live, and now my life is done.

¶ Tennyson's greatest poem was *In Memoriam*, lyrics occasioned by the death of his friend Arthur Henry Hallam.

From IN MEMORIAM

Alfred, Lord Tennyson (1809–1892)

Dark house, by which once more I stand
　　Here in the long unlovely street,
　　　Doors, where my heart was used to beat
So quickly, waiting for a hand,

A hand that can be clasp'd no more—
　　Behold me, for I cannot sleep,
　　　And like a guilty thing I creep
At earliest morning to the door.

He is not here; but far away
　　The noise of life begins again,
　　　And ghastly thro' the drizzling rain
On the bald street breaks the blank day.

． ． ．

Tonight the winds begin to rise
　　And roar from yonder dropping day:
　　　The last red leaf is whirl'd away,
The rooks are blown about the skies;

[133]

The forest crack'd, the waters curl'd,
    The cattle huddled on the lea;
    And wildly dash'd on tower and tree
The sunbeam strikes along the world:

And but for fancies, which aver
    That all thy motions gently pass
    Athwart a plane of molten glass,
I scarce could brook the strain and stir

That makes the barren branches loud;
    And but for fear it is not so,
    The wild unrest that lives in woe
Would dote and pore on yonder cloud

That rises upward always higher,
    And onward drags a laboring breast,
    And topples round the dreary west,
A looming bastion fringed with fire.

. . .

Now fades the last long streak of snow,
    Now burgeons every maze of quick
    About the flowering squares, and thick
By ashen roots the violets blow.

Now rings the woodland loud and long,
    The distance takes a lovelier hue,
    And drown'd in yonder living blue
The lark becomes a sightless song.

Now dance the lights on lawn and lea,
    The flocks are whiter down the vale,
    And milkier every milky sail
On winding stream or distant sea;

Where now the seamew pipes, or dives
    In yonder greening gleam, and fly
    The happy birds, that change their sky
To build and brood; that live their lives

From land to land; and in my breast
   Spring wakens too; and my regret
   Becomes an April violet,
And buds and blossoms like the rest.

¶ Sometimes a poet writes of someone else's death, and is moved to think of his own. William Cowper thought of himself as a "castaway"—doomed to everlasting punishment—and wrote to make the comparison.

THE CASTAWAY

William Cowper (1731–1800)

Obscurest night involved the sky,
   The Atlantic billows roared,
When such a destined wretch as I,
   Washed headlong from on board,
Of friends, of hope, of all bereft,
His floating home for ever left.

No braver chief could Albion boast
   Than he with whom he went,
Nor ever ship left Albion's coast,
   With warmer wishes sent.
He loved them both, but both in vain,
Nor him beheld, nor her again.

Not long beneath the whelming brine,
   Expert to swim, he lay;

Albion: England

[135]

Nor soon he felt his strength decline,
    Or courage die away;
But waged with death a lasting strife,
Supported by despair of life.

He shouted: nor his friends had failed
    To check the vessel's course,
But so the furious blast prevailed,
    That, pitiless perforce,
They left their outcast mate behind,
And scudded still before the wind.

Some succor yet they could afford;
    And, such as storms allow,
The cask, the coop, the floated cord,
    Delayed not to bestow.
But he (they knew) nor ship, nor shore,
Whate'er they gave, should visit more.

Nor, cruel as it seemed, could he
    Their haste himself condemn,
Aware that flight, in such a sea,
    Alone could rescue them;
Yet bitter felt it still to die
Deserted, and his friends so nigh.

He long survives, who lives an hour
    In ocean, self-upheld;
And so long he, with unspent power,
    His destiny repelled;
And ever, as the minutes flew,
Entreated help, or cried—Adieu!

At length, his transient respite past,
    His comrades, who before
Had heard his voice in every blast,
    Could catch the sound no more.
For then, by toil subdued, he drank
The stifling wave, and then he sank.

No poet wept him: but the page
    Of narrative sincere,
That tells his name, his worth, his age,
    Is wet with Anson's tear.
And tears by bards or heroes shed
Alike immortalize the dead.

I therefore purpose not, or dream,
    Descanting on his fate,
To give the melancholy theme
    A more enduring date:
But misery still delights to trace
Its semblance in another's case.

No voice divine the storm allayed,
    No light propitious shone;
When, snatched from all effectual aid,
    We perished, each alone:
But I beneath a rougher sea,
And whelmed in deeper gulfs than he.

"BREAK, BREAK, BREAK"

Alfred, Lord Tennyson (1809–1892)

ॐ

Break, break, break,
    On thy cold gray stones, O Sea!
And I would that my tongue could utter
    The thoughts that arise in me.

O well for the fisherman's boy,
    That he shouts with his sister at play!
O well for the sailor lad,
    That he sings in his boat on the bay!

Anson: famous English voyager, 1697–1762

[137]

And the stately ships go on
    To their haven under the hill;
But O for the touch of a vanish'd hand,
    And the sound of a voice that is still!

Break, break, break,
    At the foot of thy crags, O sea!
But the tender grace of a day that is dead
    Will never come back to me.

REQUIEM

Robert Louis Stevenson (1850–1894)

Under the wide and starry sky,
Dig the grave and let me lie.
Glad did I live and gladly die,
    And I laid me down with a will.

This be the verse you grave for me:
Here he lies where he longed to be;
Home is the sailor, home from sea,
    And the hunter home from the hill.

THE NIGHT-WIND

Emily Brontë (1818–1848)

In summer's mellow midnight,
A cloudless moon shone through
Our open parlor window
And rose trees wet with dew.

[138]

I sat in silent musing,
The soft wind waved my hair:
It told me Heaven was glorious,
And sleeping Earth was fair.

I needed not its breathing
To bring such thoughts to me,
But still it whispered lowly,
"How dark the woods will be!

"The thick leaves in my murmur
Are rustling like a dream,
And all their myriad voices
Instinct with spirit seem."

I said "Go, gentle singer,
Thy wooing voice is kind,
But do not think its music
Has power to reach my mind.

"Play with the scented flower,
The young tree's supple bough,
And leave my human feelings
In their own course to flow."

The wanderer would not leave me;
Its kiss grew warmer still—
"O come," it sighed so sweetly,
"I'll win thee 'gainst thy will.

"Have we not been from childhood friends?
Have I not loved thee long?
As long as thou hast loved the night
Whose silence wakes my song.

"And when thy heart is laid at rest
Beneath the church-yard stone
I shall have time enough to mourn
And thou to be alone."

TO AN ATHLETE DYING YOUNG

A. E. Housman (1859–1936)

The time you won your town the race
We chaired you through the market-place;
Man and boy stood cheering by,
And home we brought you shoulder-high.

Today, the road all runners come,
Shoulder-high we bring you home,
And set you at your threshold down,
Townsman of a stiller town.

Smart lad, to slip betimes away
From fields where glory does not stay,
And early though the laurel grows
It withers quicker than the rose.

Eyes the shady night has shut
Cannot see the record cut,
And silence sounds no worse than cheers
After earth has stopped the ears:

Now you will not swell the rout
Of lads that wore their honors out,
Runners whom renown outran
And the name died before the man.

So set, before its echoes fade,
The fleet foot on the sill of shade,
And hold to the low lintel up
The still-defended challenge-cup.

And round that early-laurelled head
Will flock to gaze the strengthless dead,

And find unwithered on its curls
The garland briefer than a girl's.

¶ The next poem will be puzzling if you ask the wrong questions of it. A woman is dead and her acquaintances mourn her. As for the emperor of ice-cream—he is just the emperor of ice-cream, that's all.

THE EMPEROR OF ICE-CREAM

Wallace Stevens (1879–1955)

Call the roller of big cigars,
The muscular one, and bid him whip
In kitchen cups concupiscent curds.
Let the wenches dawdle in such dress
As they are used to wear, and let the boys
Bring flowers in last month's newspapers.
Let be be finale of seem.
The only emperor is the emperor of ice-cream.

Take from the dresser of deal,
Lacking the three glass knobs, that sheet
On which she embroidered fantails once
And spread it so as to cover her face.
If her horny feet protrude, they come
To show how cold she is, and dumb.
Let the lamp affix its beam.
The only emperor is the emperor of ice-cream.

¶ Thomas Nashe wrote the next poem when the bubonic plague was ravaging England.

"ADIEU, FAREWELL EARTH'S BLISS"

Thomas Nashe (1567–1601?)

Adieu, farewell, earth's bliss!
This world uncertain is:
Fond are life's lustful joys,
Death proves them all but toys,
None from his darts can fly;
I am sick, I must die.
    Lord, have mercy on us!

Rich men, trust not in wealth,
Gold cannot buy you health;
Physic himself must fade,
All things to end are made.
The plague full swift goes by;
I am sick, I must die.
    Lord, have mercy on us!

Beauty is but a flower
Which wrinkles will devour;
Brightness falls from the air,
Queens have died young and fair,
Dust hath closed Helen's eye;
I am sick, I must die.
    Lord, have mercy on us!

Strength stoops unto the grave,
Worms feed on Hector brave,
Swords may not fight with fate,
Earth still holds ope her gate. .
Come! come! the bells do cry.

physic: medicine

[142]

I am sick, I must die.
      Lord, have mercy on us!

Wit with his wantonness
Tasteth death's bitterness;
Hell's executioner
Hath no ears for to hear
What vain art can reply:
I am sick, I must die.
      Lord, have mercy on us!

Haste, therefore, each degree
To welcome destiny.
Heaven is our heritage,
Earth but a player's stage;
Mount we unto the sky.
I am sick, I must die.
      Lord, have mercy on us!

"DEATH BE NOT PROUD . . ."

John Donne (1573–1631)

Death, be not proud, though some have callèd thee
Mighty and dreadful, for thou art not so;
For those whom thou think'st thou dost overthrow
Die not, poor Death; nor yet canst thou kill me.
From rest and sleep, which but thy pictures be,
Much pleasure; then from thee much more must flow:
And soonest our best men with thee do go,
Rest of their homes, and souls' delivery.
Thou'rt slave to fate, chance, kings, and desperate men,
And dost with poison, war, and sickness dwell,
And poppy or charms can make us sleep as well
And better than thy stroke. Why swell'st thou then?

One short sleep past, we wake eternally,
And Death shall be no more: Death, thou shalt die!

¶ The most famous English poem about mortality is
Thomas Gray's *Elegy Written in a Country Churchyard*.
Notice the slow and stately movement of his four-line
stanzas—each complete in itself, and pausing at the end of
each line. Some critics now refer to this stanza form as
the "elegiac quatrain."

ELEGY WRITTEN IN A
COUNTRY CHURCHYARD

Thomas Gray (1716–1771)

The curfew tolls the knell of parting day,
    The lowing herd winds slowly o'er the lea,
The ploughman homeward plods his weary way,
    And leaves the world to darkness and to me.

Now fades the glimmering landscape on the sight,
    And all the air a solemn stillness holds,
Save where the beetle wheels his droning flight,
    And drowsy tinklings lull the distant folds;

Save that from yonder ivy-mantled tower
    The moping owl does to the moon complain
Of such as, wandering near her secret bower,
    Molest her ancient solitary reign.

Beneath those rugged elms, that yew-tree's shade
    Where heaves the turf in many a mouldering heap,
Each in his narrow cell for ever laid,
    The rude Forefathers of the hamlet sleep.

The breezy call of incense-breathing morn,
    The swallow twittering from the straw-built shed,
The cock's shrill clarion, or the echoing horn,
    No more shall rouse them from their lowly bed.

For them no more the blazing hearth shall burn,
    Or busy housewife ply her evening care;
No children run to lisp their sire's return,
    Or climb his knees the envied kiss to share.

Oft did the harvest to their sickle yield,
    Their furrow oft the stubborn glebe has broke;
How jocund did they drive their team afield!
    How bow'd the woods beneath their sturdy stroke!

Let not Ambition mock their useful toil,
    Their homely joys, and destiny obscure;
Nor Grandeur hear, with a disdainful smile,
    The short and simple annals of the Poor.

The boast of heraldry, the pomp of power,
    And all that beauty, all that wealth e'er gave,
Awaits alike th' inevitable hour.
    The paths of glory lead but to the grave.

Nor you, ye Proud, impute to these the fault,
    If Memory o'er their tomb no trophies raise,
Where through the long-drawn aisle and fretted vault
    The pealing anthem swells the note of praise.

Can storied urn or animated bust
    Back to its mansion call the fleeting breath?
Can Honor's voice provoke the silent dust,
    Or Flattery soothe the dull cold ear of Death?

Perhaps in this neglected spot is laid
    Some heart once pregnant with celestial fire;
Hands, that the rod of empire might have sway'd,
    Or waked to ecstasy the living lyre.

But Knowledge to their eyes her ample page
    Rich with the spoils of time, did ne'er unroll;
Chill Penury repressed their noble rage,
    And froze the genial current of the soul.

Full many a gem of purest ray serene
    The dark unfathomed caves of ocean bear;
Full many a flower is born to blush unseen,
    And waste its sweetness on the desert air.

Some village Hampden, that with dauntless breast
    The little tyrant of his fields withstood;
Some mute inglorious Milton here may rest,
    Some Cromwell, guiltless of his country's blood.

Th' applause of listening senates to command,
    The threats of pain and ruin to despise,
To scatter plenty o'er a smiling land,
    And read their history in a nation's eyes,

Their lot forbade: nor circumscribed alone
    Their growing virtues, but their crimes confined;
Forbade to wade through slaughter to a throne,
    And shut the gates of mercy on mankind;

The struggling pangs of conscious truth to hide,
    To quench the blushes of ingenuous shame,
Or heap the shrine of Luxury and Pride
    With incense kindled at the Muse's flame.

Far from the madding crowd's ignoble strife,
    Their sober wishes never learned to stray;
Along the cool sequestered vale of life
    They kept the noiseless tenor of their way.

Yet e'en these bones from insult to protect
    Some frail memorial still erected nigh,
With uncouth rhymes and shapeless sculpture deck'd,
    Implores the passing tribute of a sigh.

Their name, their years, spelt by th' unletter'd Muse,
　　The place of fame and elegy supply;
And many a holy text around she strews,
　　That teach the rustic moralist to die.

For who, to dumb forgetfulness a prey,
　　This pleasing anxious being e'er resigned,
Left the warm precincts of the cheerful day,
　　Nor cast one longing lingering look behind?

On some fond breast the parting soul relies,
　　Some pious drops the closing eye requires;
E'en from the tomb the voice of Nature cries,
　　E'en in our ashes live their wonted fires.

For thee, who mindful of th' unhonor'd dead,
　　Dost in these lines their artless tale relate;
If chance, by lonely contemplation led,
　　Some kindred spirit shall inquire thy fate,—

Haply some hoary-headed swain may say,
　　"Oft have we seen him at the peep of dawn
Brushing with hasty steps the dews away,
　　To meet the sun upon the upland lawn.

There at the foot of yonder nodding beech
　　That wreathes its old fantastic roots so high,
His listless length at noontide would he stretch,
　　And pore upon the brook that babbles by.

Hard by yon wood, now smiling as in scorn,
　　Muttering his wayward fancies he would rove,
Now drooping, woeful-wan, like one forlorn,
　　Or crazed with care, or crossed in hopeless love.

One morn I missed him on the customed hill,
　　Along the heath, and near his favorite tree;
Another came; nor yet beside the rill,
　　Nor up the lawn, nor at the wood was he;

[147]

The next with dirges due in sad array
        Slow through the church-way path we saw him borne,
Approach and read (for thou can'st read) the lay,
        Graved on the stone beneath yon aged thorn."

The Epitaph

Here rests his head upon the lap of Earth
        A Youth to Fortune and to Fame unknown.
Fair Science frowned not on his humble birth,
        And Melancholy marked him for her own.

Large was his bounty, and his soul sincere,
        Heaven did a recompense as largely send:
He gave to Misery all he had, a tear,
        He gained from Heaven ('twas all he wished) a friend.

No farther seek his merits to disclose,
        Or draw his frailties from their dread abode,
(There they alike in trembling hope repose,)
        The bosom of his Father and his God.

¶ Again and again the poet discovers the particular fear of death in the general theme of death. Gerard Manley Hopkins, who was a Jesuit priest, addressed the next poem "To a Young Child."

SPRING AND FALL

Gerard Manley Hopkins (1844–1889)

Margaret, are you grieving
Over Goldengrove unleaving?

Leaves, like the things of man, you
With your fresh thoughts care for, can you?
Ah! as the heart grows older
It will come to such sights colder
By and by, nor spare a sigh
Though worlds of wanwood leafmeal lie;
And yet you will weep and know why.
Now no matter, child, the name:
Sorrow's springs are the same.
Nor mouth had, no nor mind, expressed
What heart heard of, ghost guessed:
It is the blight man was born for,
It is Margaret you mourn for.

"THE HEART ASKS PLEASURE FIRST"

Emily Dickinson (1830–1886)

᠌ᢒᠥ ᢗᠣ᠌

The heart asks pleasure first;
And then, excuse from pain;
And then, those little anodynes
That deaden suffering;

And then, to go to sleep;
And then, if it should be
The will of its Inquisitor,
The liberty to die.

¶ And sometimes the poet is full only of a general regret, a nostalgic elegy for all that is past.

---

[149]

"TEARS, IDLE TEARS"

Alfred, Lord Tennyson (1809–1892)

Tears, idle tears, I know not what they mean,
Tears from the depth of some divine despair
Rise in the heart, and gather to the eyes,
In looking on the happy Autumn-fields,
And thinking of the days that are no more.

Fresh as the first beam glittering on a sail,
That brings our friends up from the underworld,
Sad as the last which reddens over one
That sinks with all we love below the verge;
So sad, so fresh, the days that are no more.

Ah, sad and strange as in dark summer dawns
The earliest pipe of half-awaken'd birds
To dying ears, when unto dying eyes
The casement slowly grows a glimmering square;
So sad, so strange, the days that are no more.

Dear as remember'd kisses after death,
And sweet as those by hopeless fancy feign'd
On lips that are for others; deep as love,
Deep as first love, and wild with all regret;
O Death in Life, the days that are no more.

THE POPLAR FIELD

William Cowper (1731–1800)

The poplars are felled, farewell to the shade
And the whispering sound of the cool colonnade;
The winds play no longer, and sing in the leaves,
Nor Ouse on his bosom their image receives.

Twelve years have elapsed since I first took a view
Of my favorite field and the bank where they grew,
And now in the grass behold they are laid,
And the tree is my seat that once lent me a shade.

The blackbird has fled to another retreat
Where the hazels afford him a screen from the heat,
And the scene where his melody charmed me before,
Resounds with his sweet-flowing ditty no more.

My fugitive years are all hasting away,
And I must ere long lie as lowly as they,
With a turf on my breast, and a stone at my head,
Ere another such grove shall arise in its stead.

'Tis a sight to engage me, if anything can,
To muse on the perishing pleasures of man;
Though his life be a dream, his enjoyments, I see,
Have a being less durable even than he.

THE OLD FAMILIAR FACES

Charles Lamb (1775–1834)

ई ५

I have had playmates, I have had companions,
In my days of childhood, in my joyful schooldays,—
All, all are gone, the old familiar faces.

I have been laughing, I have been carousing,
Drinking late, sitting late, with my bosom cronies,—
All, all are gone, the old familiar faces.

I loved a love once, fairest among women;
Closed are her doors on me, I must not see her,—
All, all are gone, the old familiar faces.

I have a friend, a kinder friend has no man;
Like an ingrate, I left my friend abruptly;
Left him, to muse on the old familiar faces.

Ghost-like I paced round the haunts of my childhood,
Earth seemed a desert I was bound to traverse,
Seeking to find the old familiar faces.

Friend of my bosom, thou more than a brother,
Why wert not thou born in my father's dwelling?
So might we talk of the old familiar faces—

How some they have died, and some they have left me,
And some are taken from me; all are departed,—
All, all are gone, the old familiar faces.

DURING WIND AND RAIN

Thomas Hardy (1840–1928)

෩෨ ෫෨

They sing their dearest songs—
He, she, all of them—yea,
Treble and tenor and bass,
    And one to play;
With the candles mooning each face. . . .
    Ah, no; the years O!
How the sick leaves reel down in throngs!

They clear the creeping moss—
Elders and juniors—aye,
Making the pathways neat
    And the garden gay;
And they build a shady seat. . . .
    Ah, no; the years, the years;
See, the white storm-birds wing across!

They are blithely breakfasting all—
Men and maidens—yea,
Under the summer tree,
    With a glimpse of the bay,
While pet fowl come to the knee. . . .
    Ah, no; the years O!
And the rotten rose is ript from the wall.

They change to a high new house,
He, she, all of them—aye,
Clocks and carpets and chairs

    On the lawn all day,
And brightest things that are theirs. . . .
    Ah, no; the years, the years;
Down their carved names the raindrop ploughs.

THE WAY THROUGH THE WOODS

Rudyard Kipling (1865–1936)

They shut the road through the woods
    Seventy years ago.
Weather and rain have undone it again,
    And now you would never know
There was once a road through the woods
    Before they planted the trees.
It is underneath the coppice and heath
    And the thin anemones.
    Only the keeper sees
That, where the ring-dove broods,
    And the badgers roll at ease,
There was once a road through the woods.

Yet, if you enter the woods
    Of a summer evening late,
When the night-air cools on the trout-ringed pools
    Where the otter whistles his mate
(They fear not men in the woods,
    Because they see so few)
You will hear the beat of a horse's feet
    And the swish of a skirt in the dew,
    Steadily cantering though
The misty solitudes,
    As though they perfectly knew
The old lost road through the woods. . . .
But there is no road through the woods.

"LET BE AT LAST"

Ernest Dowson (1867–1900)

ૐ ❧

Let be at last; give over words and sighing,
    Vainly were all things said:
Better at last to find a place for lying,
    Only dead.

Silence were best, with songs and sighing over;
    Now be the music mute;
Now let the dead, red leaves of autumn cover
    A vain lute.

Silence is best; for ever and for ever,
    We will go down and sleep,
Somewhere beyond her ken, where she need never
    Come to weep.

Let be at last: colder she grows and colder;
    Sleep and the night were best;
Lying at last where we can not behold her,
    We may rest.

"THEY ARE NOT LONG"

Ernest Dowson (1867–1900)

ૐ ❧

They are not long, the weeping and the laughter,
    Love and desire and hate:
I think they have no portion in us after
    We pass the gate.

They are not long, the days of wine and roses:
    Out of a misty dream
Our path emerges for a while, then closes
    Within a dream.

THE HOUSE ON THE HILL

Edwin Arlington Robinson (*1869–1935*)

They are all gone away
    The House is shut and still,
There is nothing more to say.

Through broken walls and gray
    The winds blow bleak and shrill:
They are all gone away.

Nor is there one today
    To speak them good or ill:
There is nothing more to say.

Why is it then we stray
    Around that sunken sill?
They are all gone away,

And our poor fancy-play
    For them is wasted skill:
There is nothing more to say.

There is ruin and decay
    In the House on the Hill:
They are all gone away,
There is nothing more to say.

THE FLOWER-FED BUFFALOES

Vachel Lindsay (1879–1931)

ह≈ ≈ह

The flower-fed buffaloes of the spring
In the days of long ago,
Ranged where the locomotives sing
And the prairie flowers lie low;
The tossing, blooming, perfumed grass
Is swept away by wheat,
Wheat and wheels and wheels spin by
In the spring that still is sweet.
But the flower-fed buffaloes of the spring
Left us long ago.
They gore no more, they bellow no more,
They trundle around the hills no more:—
With the Blackfeet lying low,
With the Pawnees lying low.

¶ The other great subject is love. Often a poet combines
the two in the same poem.

"WHEN I AM DEAD, MY DEAREST"—SONG

Christina Rossetti (1830–1894)

ह≈ ≈ह

When I am dead, my dearest,
Sing no sad songs for me;
Plant thou no roses at my head,
Nor shady cypress tree:

[157]

Be the green grass above me
    With showers and dewdrops wet:
And if thou wilt, remember,
    And if thou wilt, forget.

I shall not see the shadows,
    I shall not feel the rain;
I shall not hear the nightingale
    Sing on, as if in pain:
And dreaming through the twilight
    That doth not rise nor set,
Haply I may remember,
    And haply may forget.

EARLY IN THE MORNING

Louis Simpson (1923–)

৽৽ ৶

Early in the morning
The dark Queen said,
"The trumpets are warning
There's trouble ahead."
Spent with carousing,
With wine-soaked wits,
Antony drowsing
Whispered, "It's
Too cold a morning
To get out of bed."

The army's retreating,
The fleet has fled,
Caesar is beating
His drums through the dead.
"Antony, horses!

[158]

We'll get away,
Gather our forces
For another day . . ."
"It's a cold morning,"
Antony said.

Caesar Augustus
Cleared his phlegm.
"Corpses disgust us.
Cover them."
Caesar Augustus
In his time lay
Dying, and just as
Cold as they,
On the cold morning
Of a cold day.

¶ More common is the invitation to love, the plea to "Gather ye rose-buds," or to abandon coyness. Christopher Marlowe wrote one such invitation, and Sir Walter Raleigh wrote the lady's reply.

THE PASSIONATE SHEPHERD TO HIS LOVE

Christopher Marlowe (1564–1593)

᠄᠂᠂᠂

Come live with me, and be my Love,
And we will all the pleasures prove,
That valley groves, hills and fields,
Woods, or steep mountain yields.

And we will sit upon the rocks,
Seeing the shepherds feed their flocks,

By shallow rivers, to whose falls,
Melodious birds sing madrigals.

And I will make thee beds of roses,
And a thousand fragrant posies,
A cap of flowers, and a kirtle,
Embroidered all with leaves of myrtle.

A gown made of the finest wool,
Which from our pretty lambs we pull,
Fair linèd slippers for the cold:
With buckles of the purest gold.

A belt of straw, and ivy buds,
With coral clasps and amber studs,
And if these pleasures may thee move,
Come live with me, and be my Love.

The shepherd's swains shall dance and sing,
For thy delight each May morning,
If these delights thy mind may move;
Then live with me, and be my Love.

THE NYMPH'S REPLY TO THE SHEPHERD

Sir Walter Raleigh (1552–1618)

❧ ☙

If all the world and love were young,
And truth in every shepherd's tongue,
These pretty pleasures might me move,
To live with thee and be thy Love.

Time drives the flocks from field to fold,
When rivers rage, and rocks grow cold;

And Philomel becometh dumb;
The rest complain of cares to come.

The flowers do fade, and wanton fields
To wayward winter reckoning yields;
A honey tongue, a heart of gall,
Is fancy's spring, but sorrow's fall.

Thy gowns, thy shoes, thy beds of roses,
Thy cap, thy kirtle, and thy posies,
Soon break, soon wither, soon forgotten;
In folly ripe, in reason rotten.

Thy belt of straw and ivy buds,
Thy coral clasps and amber studs,
All these in me no means can move,
To come to thee and be thy Love.

But could youth last, and love still breed,
Had joys no date, nor age no need,
Then these delights my mind might move
To live with thee and be thy Love.

"GATHER YE ROSE-BUDS . . ."

Robert Herrick (1591–1674)

ৰ৯ ৶৭

Gather ye rose-buds while ye may,
    Old Time is still a-flying:
And this same flower that smiles today,
    Tomorrow will be dying.

Philomel: the nightingale

[161]

The glorious Lamp of Heaven, the Sun,
    The higher he's a-getting,
The sooner will his race be run,
    And nearer he's to setting.

That age is best which is the first,
    When youth and blood are warmer;
But being spent, the worse, and worst
    Times, still succeed the former.

Then be not coy, but use your time;
    And while ye may, go marry:
For having lost but once your prime,
    You may for ever tarry.

TO HIS COY MISTRESS

Andrew Marvell (1621–1678)

હ્ય ઙ્

Had we but world enough, and time,
This coyness, Lady, were no crime.
We would sit down and think which way
To walk and pass our long love's day.
Thou by the Indian Ganges' side
Shouldst rubies find; I by the tide
Of Humber would complain. I would
Love you ten years before the Flood,
And you should, if you please, refuse
Till the conversion of the Jews.
My vegetable love should grow
Vaster than empires, and more slow;
An hundred years should go to praise
Thine eyes, and on thy forehead gaze,
Two hundred to adore each breast,

But thirty thousand to the rest;
An age at least to every part,
And the last age should show your heart.
For, Lady, you deserve this state,
Nor would I love at lower rate.
        But at my back I always hear
Time's wingèd chariot hurrying near;
And yonder all before us lie
Deserts of vast eternity.
Thy beauty shall no more be found,
Nor, in thy marble vault, shall sound
My echoing song; then worms shall try
That long preserved virginity,
And your quaint honor turn to dust,
And into ashes all my lust:
The grave's a fine and private place,
But none, I think, do there embrace.
        Now therefore, while the youthful hue
Sits on thy skin like morning dew,
And while thy willing soul transpires
At every pore with instant fires,
Now let us sport us while we may,
And now, like amorous birds of prey,
Rather at once our time devour
Than languish in his slow-chapt power.
Let us roll all our strength and all
Our sweetness up into one ball,
And tear our pleasures with rough strife
Thorough the iron gates of life;
Thus, though we cannot make our sun
Stand still, yet we will make him run.

"GO, LOVELY ROSE"

Edmund Waller (1606–1687)

Go, lovely Rose,
Tell her, that wastes her time and me,
That now she knows,
When I resemble her to thee,
How sweet and fair she seems to be.

Tell her that's young
And shuns to have her graces spied,
That hadst thou sprung
In deserts, where no men abide,
Thou must have uncommended died.

Small is the worth
Of beauty from the light retired;
Bid her come forth,
Suffer herself to be desired,
And not blush so to be admired.

Then die, that she
The common fate of all things rare
May read in thee;
How small a part of time they share
That are so wondrous sweet and fair!

"IN THE MERRY MONTH OF MAY"

Nicholas Breton (1545–1626)

In the merry month of May,
In a morn by break of day,
Forth I walked by the wood side,
Wheras May was in his pride.
There I spièd all alone
Phyllida and Corydon.
Much ado there was, God wot!
He would love and she would not.
She said, Never man was true;
He said, None was false to you.
He said, He had loved her long;
She said, Love should have no wrong.
Corydon would kiss her then;
She said, Maids must kiss no men
Till they did for good and all.
Then she made the shepherd call
All the heavens to witness truth,
Never loved a truer youth.
Thus with many a pretty oath,
Yea and nay, and faith and troth,
Such as silly shepherds use,
When they will not love abuse,
Love, which had been long deluded,
Was with kisses sweet concluded:
And Phyllida with garlands gay
Was made the Lady of the May.

"AS YOU CAME FROM THE HOLY LAND . . ."

Sir Walter Raleigh (1552–1618)

"As you came from the holy land
   Of Walsingham,
Met you not with my true love
   By the way as you came?"

"How shall I know your true love,
   That have met many one,
As I went to the holy land,
   That have come, that have gone?"

"She is neither white nor brown,
   But as the heavens fair;
There is none hath a form so divine
   In the earth or the air."

"Such an one did I meet, good Sir,
   Such an angelic face,
Who like a queen, like a nymph, did appear
   By her gate, by her grace."

"She hath left me here all alone,
   All alone, as unknown,
Who sometimes did me lead with herself,
   And me loved as her own."

"What's the cause that she leaves you alone,
   And a new way doth take:
Who loved you once as her own,
   And her joy did you make?"

"I have loved her all my youth,
   But now old, as you see:
Love likes not the falling fruit
   From the withered tree.

"Know that love is a careless child,
     And forgets promise past;
He is blind, he is deaf when he list,
     And in faith never fast.

"His desire is a dureless content,
     And a trustless joy;
He is won with a world of despair,
     And is lost with a toy.

"Of womenkind such indeed is the love,
     Or the word love abused,
Under which many childish desires
     And conceits are excused.

"But true love is a durable fire,
     In the mind ever burning,
Never sick, never old, never dead,
     From itself never turning."

¶ Love happy, and love unhappy. Love invited and love dismissed. Any version of love is a concern of the poet.

"SINCE THERE'S NO HELP"

Michael Drayton (1563–1631)

Since there's no help, come let us kiss and part;
Nay, I have done, you get no more of me;
And I am glad, yea, glad with all my heart
And thus so cleanly I myself can free;
Shake hands for ever, cancel all our vows,

And when we meet at any time again,
Be it not seen in either of our brows
That we one jot of former love retain.
Now at the last gasp of love's latest breath,
When, his pulse failing, passion speechless lies,
When faith is kneeling by his bed of death,
And innocence is closing up his eyes,
     Now, if thou would'st, when all have given him over,
     From death to life thou might'st him yet recover!

"LEAVE ME, O LOVE . . ."

Sir Philip Sidney (1554–1586)

Leave me, O Love, which reachest but to dust,
And thou, my mind, aspire to higher things!
Grow rich in that which never taketh rust,
Whatever fades, but fading pleasure brings.
Draw in thy beams, and humble all thy might
To that sweet yoke where lasting freedoms be;
Which breaks the clouds and opens forth the light,
That doth both shine and give us sight to see.
O take fast hold; let that light be thy guide
In this small course which birth draws out to death,
And think how evil becometh him to slide
Who seeketh heaven, and comes of heavenly breath.
     Then farewell, world! thy uttermost I see:
     Eternal Love, maintain thy life in me!

"THE EARTH LATE CHOKED
WITH SHOWERS"

Thomas Lodge (1557–1625)

ঙ৯ ৶ঙ

The earth, late choked with showers,
  Is now arrayed in green;
Her bosom springs with flowers,
  The air dissolves her teen.
The heavens laugh at her glory,
Yet bide I sad and sorry.

The woods are decked with leaves
  And trees are clothed gay,
And Flora, crowned with sheaves,
  With oaken boughs doth play;
Where I am clad in black,
The token of my wrack.

The birds upon the trees
  Do sing with pleasant voices,
And chant in their degrees
  Their loves and lucky choices;
When I, whilst they are singing,
With sighs mine arms am wringing.

The thrushes seek the shade,
  And I my fatal grave;
Their flight to heaven is made,
  My walk on earth I have;
They free, I thrall; they jolly,
I sad and pensive wholly.

teen: grief   *Flora:* goddess of flowers

[169]

"WHEN THOU MUST HOME"

Thomas Campion (1567–1620)

୫~ ෫ى

When thou must home to shades of underground,
    And there arrived, a new admirèd guest,
The beauteous spirits do engirt thee round,
    White Iope, blithe Helen and the rest,
To hear the story of thy finished love
From that smooth tongue, whose music hell can move,

Then wilt thou speak of banqueting delights,
    Of masks and revels which sweet youth did make,
Of tourneys and great challenges of knights,
    And all these triumphs for thy beauty's sake;
When thou has told these honors done to thee,
Then tell, O! tell, how thou didst murder me.

SONG, TO CELIA

Ben Jonson (1573–1637)

୫~ ෫ى

Drink to me only with thine eyes,
    And I will pledge with mine;
Or leave a kiss but in the cup
    And I'll not look for wine.
The thirst that from the soul doth rise
    Doth ask a drink divine;
But might I of Jove's nectar sup,
    I would not change for thine.
I sent thee late a rosy wreath,
    Not so much honoring thee,

As giving it a hope that there
 It could not withered be.
But thou thereon didst only breathe,
 And sent'st it back to me,
Since when it grows, and smells, I swear,
 Not of itself but thee!

DELIGHT IN DISORDER

Robert Herrick (1591–1674)

A sweet disorder in the dress
Kindles in clothes a wantonness:
A lawn about the shoulders thrown
Into a fine distraction;
An erring lace, which here and there
Enthrals the crimson stomacher;
A cuff neglectful, and thereby
Ribbands to flow confusedly;
A winning wave, deserving note
In the tempestuous petticoat;
A careless shoe-string, in whose tie
I see a wild civility,
Do more bewitch me, than when art
Is too precise in every part.

"HIS GOLDEN LOCKS TIME HATH TO SILVER TURNED"

George Peele (1557–1596)

ও~ ৩

His golden locks time hath to silver turned;
    O time too swift, O swiftness never ceasing!
His youth 'gainst time and age hath ever spurned,
    But spurned in vain; youth waneth by increasing.
Beauty, strength, youth, are flowers but fading seen;
Duty, faith, love, are roots, and ever green.

His helmet now shall make a hive for bees,
    And lovers' sonnets turned to holy psalms,
A man-at-arms must now serve on his knees,
    And feed on prayers, which are age's alms;
But though from court to cottage he depart,
His saint is sure of his unspotted heart.

And when he saddest sits in homely cell,
    He'll teach his swains this carol for a song:
"Blest be the hearts that wish my sovereign well,
    Curst be the souls that think her any wrong."
Goddess, allow this agèd man his right,
To be your beadsman now, that was your knight.

beadsman: a person who prays for another

TO ALTHEA FROM PRISON

Richard Lovelace (1618–1657)

When Love with unconfinèd wings
    Hovers within my gates,
And my divine Althea brings
    To whisper at the grates;
When I lie tangled in her hair
    And fetter'd to her eye,
The birds that wanton in the air
    Know no such liberty.

When flowing cups run swiftly round
    With no allaying Thames,
Our careless heads with roses bound,
    Our hearts with loyal flames;
When thirsty grief in wine we steep,
    When healths and draughts go free,
Fishes that tipple in the deep
    Know no such liberty.

When (like committed linnets) I
    With shriller throat shall sing
The sweetness, mercy, majesty
    And glories of my King;
When I shall voice aloud how good
    He is, how great should be,
Enlargèd winds, that curl the flood,
    Know no such liberty.

Stone walls do not a prison make,
    Nor iron bars a cage;
Minds innocent and quiet take
    That for an hermitage;

If I have freedom in my love.
And in my soul am free,
Angels alone, that soar above,
Enjoy such liberty.

"OUT UPON IT, I HAVE LOVED"

Sir John Suckling (1609–1642)

Out upon it! I have loved
    Three whole days together;
And am like to love three more,
    If it prove fair weather.

Time shall moult away his wings
    Ere he shall discover
In the whole wide world again
    Such a constant lover.

But the spite on't is, no praise
    Is due at all to me;
Love with me had made no stays,
    Had it been but she.

Had it any been but she,
    And that very face,
There had been at least ere this
    A dozen in her place.

SONG

John Donne (1573–1631)

Go and catch a falling star,
    Get with child a mandrake root,
Tell me where all past years are,
    Or who cleft the devil's foot,
Teach me to hear mermaid's singing,
Or to keep off envy's stinging,
        And find
        What wind
Serves to advance an honest mind.

If thou be'st born to strange sights,
    Things invisible to see,
Ride ten thousand days and nights,
    Till age snow white hairs on thee,
Thou, when thou return'st, wilt tell me
All strange wonders that befell thee,
        And swear
        No where
Lives a woman true, and fair.

If thou find'st one, let me know;
    Such a pilgrimage were sweet;
Yet do not, I would not go,
    Though at next door we might meet.
Though she were true when you met her,
And last, till you write your letter,
        Yet she
        Will be
False, ere I come, to two or three.

JOHN ANDERSON, MY JO

Robert Burns (1759–1796)

John Anderson, my jo, John,
    When we were first acquent;
Your locks were like the raven,
    Your bonnie brow was brent;
But now your brow is bald, John,
    Your locks are like the snow;
But blessings on your frosty pow,
    John Anderson, my jo.
John Anderson, my jo, John,
    We clamb the hill thegither;
And mony a cantie day, John,
    We've had wi' ane anither:
Now we maun totter down, John,
    And hand in hand we'll go,
And sleep thegither at the foot,
    John Anderson, my jo.

A RED, RED ROSE

Robert Burns (1759–1796)

My Luve is like a red, red rose,
    That's newly sprung in June:
My Luve is like the melodie,
    That's sweetly played in tune.

acquent: acquainted   *bonnie:* handsome   *brent:* smooth   *pow:* head
cantie: cheerful

As fair art thou, my bonnie lass,
    So deep in luve am I;
And I will luve thee still, my dear,
    Till a' the seas gang dry.

Till a' the seas gang dry, my dear,
    And the rocks melt wi' the sun;
And I will luve thee still, my dear,
    While the sands o' life shall run.

And fare-thee-weel, my only luve!
    And fare-thee-weel a while!
And I will come again, my luve,
    Though it were ten thousand mile.

LOVE'S SECRET

William Blake (1757–1827)

Never seek to tell thy love,
    Love that never told can be;
For the gentle wind does move
    Silently, invisibly.

I told my love, I told my love,
    I told her all my heart;
Trembling, cold, in ghastly fears.
Ah! she did depart!

Soon as she was gone from me,
    A traveler came by,
Silently, invisibly:
He took her with a sigh.

[177]

"PAST RUINED ILION"

Walter Savage Landor (1775–1864)

৳৽ ৶ৎ

Past ruined Ilion Helen lives,
    Alcestis rises from the shades;
Verse calls them forth; 'tis verse that gives
    Immortal youth to mortal maids.

Soon shall Oblivion's deepening veil
    Hide all the peopled hills you see,
The gay, the proud, while lovers hail
    These many summers you and me.

The tear for fading beauty check
    For passing glory cease to sigh;
One form shall rise above the wreck
    One name, Ianthe, shall not die.

"SO WE'LL GO NO MORE A-ROVING"

George Gordon, Lord Byron (1788–1824)

৳৽ ৶ৎ

So we'll go no more a-roving
    So late into the night,
Though the night was made for loving,
    And the moon be still as bright.

For the sword outwears its sheath,
    And the soul wears out the breast,
And the heart must pause to breathe,
    And love itself have rest.

Though the night was made for loving
And the day returns too soon,
Yet we'll go no more a-roving
By the light of the moon.

"MUSIC, WHEN SOFT VOICES DIE"

Percy Bysshe Shelley (1792–1822)

ॐ ॐ

Music, when soft voices die,
Vibrates in the memory—
Odors, when sweet violets sicken,
Live within the sense they quicken.

Rose leaves, when the rose is dead,
Are heaped for the belovèd's bed;
And so thy thoughts, when thou art gone,
Love itself shall slumber on.

WHEN YOU ARE OLD

William Butler Yeats (1865–1939)

ॐ ॐ

When you are old and gray and full of sleep,
And nodding by the fire, take down this book,
And slowly read, and dream of the soft look
Your eyes had once, and of their shadows deep.

How many loved your moments of glad grace,
And loved your beauty with love false or true,

But one man loved the pilgrim soul in you,
And loved the sorrows of your changing face;

And bending down beside the glowing bars,
Murmur, a little sadly, how Love fled
And paced upon the mountains overhead
And hid his face amid a crowd of stars.

THE SONG OF WANDERING AENGUS

William Butler Yeats (1865–1939)

ভ৵ ৵ঽ

I went out to the hazel wood,
Because a fire was in my head,
And cut and peeled a hazel wand,
And hooked a berry to a thread;
And when white moths were on the wing,
And moth-like stars were flickering out,
I dropped the berry in a stream
And caught a little silver trout.

When I had laid it on the floor
I went to blow the fire aflame,
But something rustled on the floor,
And some one called me by my name:
It had become a glimmering girl
With apple blossom in her hair
Who called me by my name and ran
And faded through the brightening air.

Though I am old with wandering
Through hollow lands and hilly lands,
I will find out where she has gone,
And kiss her lips and take her hands;

And walk among long dappled grass,
And pluck till time and times are done
The silver apples of the moon,
The golden apples of the sun.

¶ Compare this poem by Yeats with Keats's "La Belle
Dame Sans Merci," page 6.

NO SECOND TROY

William Butler Yeats (1865–1939)

Why should I blame her that she filled my days
With misery, or that she would of late
Have taught to ignorant men most violent ways,
Or hurled the little streets upon the great,
Had they but courage equal to desire?
What could have made her peaceful with a mind
That nobleness made simple as a fire,
With beauty like a tightened bow, a kind
That is not natural in an age like this,
Being high and solitary and most stern?
Why, what could she have done being what she is?
Was there another Troy for her to burn?

FOR ANNE GREGORY

William Butler Yeats (1865–1939)

&

"Never shall a young man,
Thrown into despair
By those great honey-colored
Ramparts at your ear,
Love you for yourself alone
And not your yellow hair."

"But I can get a hair-dye
And set such color there,
Brown, or black, or carrot,
That young men in despair
May love me for myself alone
And not my yellow hair."

"I heard an old religious man
But yesternight declare
That he had found a text to prove
That only God, my dear,
Could love you for yourself alone
And not your yellow hair."

¶ These four poems by Yeats were written in the order in which they are printed. "When You Are Old" was written toward the end of the last century, and "For Anne Gregory" quite a few years into this one. Notice the development from poem to poem.

BLUE GIRLS

John Crowe Ransom (1888–   )

୫❧

Twirling your blue skirts, traveling the sward
Under the towers of your seminary,
Go listen to your teachers old and contrary
Without believing a word.

Tie the white fillets then about your hair
And think no more of what will come to pass
Than bluebirds that go walking on the grass
And chattering on the air.

Practice your beauty, blue girls, before it fail;
And I will cry with my loud lips and publish
Beauty which all our power shall never establish,
It is so frail.

For I could tell you a story which is true:
I know a lady with a terrible tongue,
Blear eyes fallen from blue,
All her perfections tarnished—yet it is not long
Since she was lovelier than any of you.

AN IMMORALITY

Ezra Pound (1885–   )

୫❧

Sing we for love and idleness,
Naught else is worth the having.

Though I have been in many a land,
There is naught else in living.

And I would rather have my sweet,
Though rose-leaves die of grieving,

Than do high deeds in Hungary
To pass all men's believing.

¶ "An Immorality" is one of Ezra Pound's early poems.
Later he translated some Chinese poems, rather freely.
The next poem is one of the loveliest.

THE RIVER-MERCHANT'S WIFE:
A LETTER

Ezra Pound (1885–)

While my hair was still cut straight across my forehead
I played about the front gate, pulling flowers.
You came by on bamboo stilts, playing horse,
You walked about my seat, playing with blue plums.
And we went on living in the village of Chokan:
Two small people, without dislike or suspicion.

At fourteen I married My Lord you.
I never laughed, being bashful.
Lowering my head, I looked at the wall.
Called to, a thousand times, I never looked back.

At fifteen I stopped scowling,
I desired my dust to be mingled with yours
Forever and forever and forever.
Why should I climb the look out?

[184]

At sixteen you departed,
You went into far Ku-to-yen, by the river of swirling eddies,
And you have been gone five months.
The monkeys make sorrowful noise overhead.

You dragged your feet when you went out.
By the gate now, the moss is grown, the different mosses,
Too deep to clear them away!
The leaves fall early this autumn, in wind.
The paired butterflies are already yellow with August
Over the grass in the West garden;
They hurt me. I grow older.
If you are coming down through the narrows of the river
    Kiang,
Please let me know beforehand,
And I will come out to meet you
                      As far as Cho-fu-Sa.

IN TIME OF 'THE BREAKING
OF NATIONS' (1915)

Thomas Hardy (1840–1928)

ॐ⇔॰ॐ

Only a man harrowing clods
    In a slow silent walk,
With an old horse that stumbles and nods
    Half asleep as they stalk.

Only thin smoke without flame
    From the heaps of couch-grass;
Yet this will go onward the same
    Though Dynasties pass.

Yonder a maid and her wight
  Come whispering by:
War's annals will cloud into night
  Ere their story die.

AT CASTLE BOTEREL

Thomas Hardy (1840–1928)

As I drive to the junction of lane and highway,
  And the drizzle bedrenches the waggonette,
I look behind at the fading byway,
  And see on its slope, now glistening wet,
    Distinctly yet

Myself and a girlish form benighted
  In dry March weather. We climb the road
Beside a chaise. We had just alighted
  To ease the sturdy pony's load,
    When he sighed and slowed.

What we did as we climbed, and what we talked of
  Matters not much, nor to what it led,—
Something that life will not be balked of
  Without rude reason till hope is dead,
    And feeling fled.

It filled but a minute. But was there ever
  A time of such quality, since or before,
In that hill's story? To one mind never,
  Though it has been climbed, foot-swift, foot-sore,
    By thousands more.

Primaeval rocks form the road's steep border,
  And much have they faced there, first and last,

Of the transitory in Earth's long order;
  But what they record in color and cast
   Is—that we two passed.

And to me, though Time's unflinching rigor,
  In mindless rote, has ruled from sight
The substance now, one phantom figure
  Remains on the slope, as when that night
   Saw us alight.

I look back and see it there, shrinking, shrinking,
  I look back at it amid the rain
For the very last time; for my sand is sinking,
  And I shall traverse old love's domain
   Never again.

¶ One of the most famous poems of modern times is
Matthew Arnold's "Dover Beach." Many people turned
similarly from the baffling nature of the cosmos and history to the consolations of private life and love.

DOVER BEACH

Matthew Arnold (1822–1888)

ϡ❧

  The sea is calm tonight,
The tide is full, the moon lies fair
Upon the straits;—on the French coast, the light
Gleams, and is gone; the cliffs of England stand,
Glimmering and vast, out in the tranquil bay.
Come to the window, sweet is the night air!
Only, from the long line of spray
Where the sea meets the moon-blanched land,

Listen! you hear the grating roar
Of pebbles which the waves draw back, and fling,
At their return, up the high strand,
Begin, and cease, and then again begin,
With tremulous cadence slow, and bring
The eternal note of sadness in.

Sophocles long ago
Heard it on the Aegean, and it brought
Into his mind the turbid ebb and flow
Of human misery; we
Find also in the sound a thought,
Hearing it by this distant northern sea.

The sea of faith
Was once, too, at the full, and round earth's shore
Lay like the folds of a bright girdle furled;
But now I only hear
Its melancholy, long, withdrawing roar,
Retreating to the breath
Of the night-wind down the vast edges drear
And naked shingles of the world.

Ah, love, let us be true
To one another! for the world, which seems
To lie before us like a land of dreams,
So various, so beautiful, so new,
Hath really neither joy, nor love, nor light,
Nor certitude, nor peace, nor help for pain;
And we are here as on a darkling plain
Swept with confused alarms of struggle and flight,
Where ignorant armies clash by night.

"AS I WALKED OUT ONE EVENING"

W. H. Auden (1907–   )

As I walked out one evening,
    Walking down Bristol Street,
The crowds upon the pavement
    Were fields of harvest wheat.

And down by the brimming river
    I heard a lover sing
Under an arch of the railway:
    "Love has no ending.

"I'll love you, dear, I'll love you
    Till China and Africa meet
And the river jumps over the mountain
    And the salmon sing in the street.

"I'll love you till the ocean
    Is folded and hung up to dry
And the seven stars go squawking
    Like geese about the sky.

"The years shall run like rabbits,
    For in my arms I hold
The Flower of the Ages
    And the first love of the world."

But all the clocks in the city
    Began to whirr and chime:
"O let not Time deceive you,
    You cannot conquer Time.

"In the burrows of the Nightmare
    Where Justice naked is,

Time watches from the shadow
 And coughs when you would kiss.

"In headaches and in worry
 Vaguely life leaks away,
And Time will have his fancy
 Tomorrow or today.

"Into many a green valley
 Drifts the appalling snow;
Time breaks the threaded dances
 And the diver's brilliant bow.

"O plunge your hands in water,
 Plunge them in up to the wrist;
Stare, stare in the basin
 And wonder what you've missed.

"The glacier knocks in the cupboard,
 The desert sighs in the bed,
And the crack in the tea-cup opens
 A lane to the land of the dead,

"Where the beggars raffle the banknotes
 And the Giant is enchanting to Jack,
And the Lily-white Boy is a Roarer
 And Jill goes down on her back.

"O look, look in the mirror,
 O look in your distress;
Life remains a blessing
 Although you cannot bless.

"O stand, stand at the window
 As the tears scald and start;
You shall love your crooked neighbor
 With your crooked heart."

It was late, late in the evening,
　　The lovers they were gone;
The clocks had ceased their chiming
　　And the deep river ran on.

¶ What the lovers hear from W. H. Auden's clock is no
love story. It is what many people would call "a philosophy," though it is not systematic like real philosophy.
Neither is it abstract and high-flown. It is an attitude toward living, derived from the experience of living. And
though poets change their minds like other men, they
usually feel as they write each poem that "there is one
story and one story only."

TO JUAN AT THE WINTER SOLSTICE

Robert Graves (1895–　)

There is one story and one story only
That will prove worth your telling,
Whether as learned bard or gifted child;
To it all lines or lesser gauds belong
That startle with their shining ·
Such common stories as they stray into.

Is it of trees you tell, their months and virtues,
Of strange beasts that beset you,
Of birds that croak at you the Triple will?
Or of the Zodiac and how slow it turns
Below the Boreal Crown,
Prison of all true kings that ever reigned?

Water to water, ark again to ark,
From woman back to woman:
So each new victim treads unfalteringly
The never altered circuit of his fate,
Bringing twelve peers as witness
Both to his starry rise and starry fall.

Or is it of the Virgin's silver beauty,
All fish below the thighs?
She in her left hand bears a leafy quince;
When with her right she crooks a finger, smiling,
How may the King hold back?
Royally then he barters life for love.

Or of the undying snake from chaos hatched,
Whose coils contain the ocean,
Into whose chops with naked sword he springs,
Then in black water, tangled by the reeds,
Battles three days and nights,
To be spewed up beside her scalloped shore?

Much snow is falling, winds roar hollowly,
The owl hoots from the elder,
Fear in your heart cries to the loving-cup:
Sorrow to sorrow as the sparks fly upward.
The log groans and confesses
There is one story and one story only.

Dwell on her graciousness, dwell on her smiling,
Do not forget what flowers
The great boar trampled down in ivy time.
Her brow was creamy as the long ninth wave,
Her sea-blue eyes were wild,
But nothing promised that is not performed.

"MY MIND TO ME A KINGDOM IS"

Sir Edward Dyer (1550–1607)

ॐ ♨

My mind to me a kingdom is;
    Such present joys therein I find
That it excels all other bliss
    That earth affords or grows by kind.
Though much I want which most would have,
Yet still my mind forbids to crave.

No princely pomp, no wealthy store,
    No force to win a victory,
No wily wit to salve a sore,
    No shape to feed a loving eye;
To none of these I yield as thrall—
For why? My mind doth serve for all.

I see how plenty surfeits oft,
    And hasty climbers soonest fall;
I see that such as are aloft
    Mishap doth threaten most of all.
They get with toil, they keep with fear;
Such cares my mind could never bear.

Content to live, this is my stay;
    I seek no more than may suffice;
I press to bear no haughty sway;
    Look, what I lack my mind supplies.
Lo, thus I triumph like a king,
Content with that my mind doth bring.

Some have too much, yet still do crave;
    I little have, and seek no more.
They are but poor, though much they have,
    And I am rich with little store.
They poor, I rich; they beg, I give;
They lack, I leave; they pine, I live.

I laugh not at another's loss;
    I grudge not at another's pain;
No worldly waves my mind can toss;
    My state at one doth still remain.
I fear no foe, I fawn no friend;
I loathe not life, nor dread my end.

Some weigh their pleasure by their lust,
    Their wisdom by their rage of will;
Their treasure is their only trust;
    A cloakèd craft their store of skill.
But all the pleasure that I find
Is to maintain a quiet mind.

My wealth is health and perfect ease;
    My conscience clear my chief defense;
I neither seek by bribes to please,
    Nor by deceit to breed offense.
Thus do I live; thus will I die;
Would all did so as well as I!

"THOU BLIND MAN'S MARK"

Sir Philip Sidney (1554–1586)

Thou blind man's mark, thou fool's self-chosen snare,
Fond fancy's scum, and dregs of scattered thought;
Band of all evils, cradle of causeless care;
Thou web of will, whose end is never wrought;
Desire, desire! I have too dearly bought,
With price of mangled mind, thy worthless ware;
Too long, too long, asleep thou hast me brought,
Who should my mind to higher things prepare.
But yet in vain thou hast my ruin sought;

In vain thou madest me to vain things aspire;
In vain thou kindlest all thy smoky fire;
For virtue hath this better lesson taught,
Within myself to seek my only hire,
Desiring nought but how to kill desire.

THE BIGHT

Elizabeth Bishop (*1911–*)

ॐ ◦ ॐ

On my birthday

At low tide like this how sheer the water is.
White, crumbling ribs of marl protrude and glare
and the boats are dry, the pilings dry as matches.
Absorbing, rather than being absorbed,
the water in the bight doesn't wet anything,
the color of the gas flame turned as low as possible.
One can smell it turning to gas; if one were Baudelaire
one could probably hear it turning to marimba music.
The little ocher dredge at work off the end of the dock
already plays the dry perfectly off-beat claves.
The birds are outsize. Pelicans crash
into this peculiar gas unnecessarily hard,
it seems to me, like pickaxes,
rarely coming up with anything to show for it,
and going off with humorous elbowings.
Black-and-white man-of-war birds soar
 on impalpable drafts
and open their tails like scissors on the curves
or tense them like wishbones, till they tremble.
The frowsy sponge boats keep coming in
with the obliging air of retrievers,
bristling with jackstraw gaffs and hooks
and decorated with bobbles of sponges.

[195]

There is a fence of chicken wire along the dock
where, glinting like little plowshares,
the blue-gray shark tails are hung up to dry
for the Chinese-restaurant trade.
Some of the little white boats are still piled up
against each other, or lie on their sides, stove in,
and not yet salvaged, if they ever will be, from the last bad
   storm,
like torn-open, unanswered letters.
The bight is littered with old correspondences.
Click, Click. Goes the dredge,
and brings up a dripping jawful of marl.
All the untidy activity continues,
awful but cheerful.

HEAVEN-HAVEN

A Nun Takes the Veil

Gerard Manley Hopkins (1844–1889)

ॐ

I have desired to go
   Where springs not fail,
To fields where flies no sharp and sided hail
   And a few lilies blow.

And I have asked to be
   Where no storms come,
Where the green swell is in the havens dumb,
   And out of the swing of the sea.

"THE MAN OF LIFE UPRIGHT . . ."

Thomas Campion (1576–1620)

The man of life upright,
  Whose guiltless heart is free
From all dishonest deeds,
  Or thought of vanity;

The man whose silent days
  In harmless joys are spent,
Whom hopes cannot delude
  Nor sorrow discontent;

That man needs neither towers
  Nor armor for defense,
Nor secret vaults to fly
  From thunder's violence!

He only can behold
  With unaffrighted eyes
The horrors of the deep
  And terrors of the skies.

Thus, scorning all the cares
  That fate or fortune brings,
He makes the heaven his book,
  His wisdom heavenly things;

Good thoughts his only friends,
  His wealth a well-spent age,
The earth his sober inn
  And quiet pilgrimage.

¶ Religion is one of the great subjects of English poetry, especially in the seventeenth century. No poet in English is more attractively pious than George Herbert.

THE PULLEY

George Herbert (1593–1633)

ঔ✣ ✤ঔ

When God at first made Man,
Having a glass of blessings standing by;
"Let us," said He, "pour on him all we can:
Let the world's riches, which dispersèd lie,
    Contract into a span."

So strength first made a way;
Then beauty flow'd, then wisdom, honor, pleasure:
When almost all was out, God made a stay,
Perceiving that alone, of all His treasure,
    Rest in the bottom lay.

"For if I should," said He,
"Bestow this jewel also on my creature,
He would adore My gifts instead of Me,
And rest in Nature, not the God of Nature:
    So both should losers be.

Yet let him keep the rest,
But keep them with repining restlessness:
Let him be rich and weary, that at least,
If goodness lead him not, yet weariness
    May toss him to My breast."

VIRTUE

George Herbert (1593–1633)

❧ ❧

Sweet day, so cool, so calm, so bright,
The bridal of the earth and sky:
The dew shall weep thy fall tonight;
    For thou must die,

Sweet rose, whose hue angry and brave
Bids the rash gazer wipe his eye,
Thy root is ever in its grave,
    And thou must die.

Sweet spring, full of sweet days and roses,
A box where sweets compacted lie,
My music shows ye have your closes,
    And all must die.

Only a sweet and virtuous soul,
Like season'd timber, never gives;
But though the whole world turn to coal,
    Then chiefly lives.

REDEMPTION

George Herbert (1593–1633)

❧ ❧

Having been tenant long to a rich Lord,
    Not thriving, I resolved to be bold,
    And make a suit unto him, to afford

A new small-rented lease, and cancel the old.
In heaven at his manor I him sought:
    They told me there, that he was lately gone
    About some land, which he had dearly bought
Long since on earth, to take possession.
I straight return'd, and knowing his great birth,
    Sought him accordingly in great resorts;
    In cities, theatres, gardens, parks, and courts:
At length I heard a ragged noise and mirth
    Of thieves and murderers: there I him espied,
    Who straight, *Your suit is granted*, said, and died.

THE ALTAR

George Herbert (1593–1633)

A broken altar, Lord, thy servant rears,
Made of a heart, and cémented with tears:
    Whose parts are as thy hand did frame;
    No workman's tool hath touched the same.
        A heart alone
        Is such a stone,
        As nothing but
        Thy power doth cut.
        Wherefore each part
        Of my hard heart
        Meets in this frame,
        To praise thy name;
    That, if I chance to hold my peace,
    These stones to praise thee may not cease.
O, let thy blessèd sacrifice be mine,
And sanctify this altar to be thine.

¶ A poem about an altar, made in the shape of an altar! Maybe it's only a trick, but it's none the less pleasing. And Herbert made another shape too.

From EASTER-WINGS

George Herbert (1593–1633)

ई॰ ॰इ

Lord, who createdst man in wealth and store,
Though foolishly he lost the same,
Decaying more and more,
Till he became
Most poor:
With thee
O let me rise
As larks, harmoniously,
And sing this day thy victories:
Then shall the fall further the flight in me.

¶ Andrew Marvell, who wrote "To His Coy Mistress," page 162, also wrote "The Garden," which is one of the loveliest poems in English. Yet it is a puzzling poem in its final meaning, because there is a constant tug of war between Marvell's obvious love of the garden and its plants and his comic disparagement of this love by exaggeration and disproportion. This tug of war makes irony, and finally you have to say that the two contradictory feelings together *are* the meaning of the poem, and that either one alone would be false. When you stop to realize how commonly our feelings (about anything) are mixed feelings, and how seldom our feelings are simple and pure, you will see why so many poems go two or more ways at once.

THE GARDEN

Andrew Marvell (1621–1678)

How vainly men themselves amaze,
To win the palm, the oak, or bays;
And their incessant labors see
Crowned from some single herb or tree,
Whose short and narrow-vergèd shade
Does prudently their toils upbraid,
While all the flowers, and trees, do close,
To weave the garlands of repose.

Fair Quiet, have I found thee here,
And Innocence, thy sister dear?
Mistaken long, I sought you then
In busy companies of men;
Your sacred plants, if here below,
Only among the plants will grow;
Society is all but rude,
To this delicious solitude.

No white nor red was ever seen
So amorous as this lovely green.
Fond lovers, cruel as their flame,
Cut in these trees their mistress' name;
Little, alas! they know or heed,
How far these beauties hers exceed!
Fair trees! where'er your barks I wound,
No name shall but your own be found.

When we have run our passions' heat
Love hither makes his best retreat.
The gods, who mortal beauty chase,
Still in a tree did end their race;
Apollo hunted Daphne so,

Only that she might laurel grow;
And Pan did after Syrinx speed,
Not as a nymph, but for a reed.

What wondrous life is this I lead!
Ripe apples drop about my head;
The luscious clusters of the vine
Upon my mouth do crush their wine;
The nectarine and curious peach,
Into my hands themselves do reach;
Stumbling on melons, as I pass,
Insnared with flowers, I fall on grass.

Meanwhile the mind, from pleasure less,
Withdraws into its happiness;
The mind, that ocean where each kind
Does straight its own resemblance find;
Yet it creates, transcending these,
Far other worlds, and other seas,
Annihilating all that's made
To a green thought in a green shade.

Here at the fountain's sliding foot,
Or at some fruit-tree's mossy root,
Casting the body's vest aside,
My soul into the boughs does glide:
There, like a bird, it sits and sings,
Then whets and claps its silver wings,
And, till prepar'd for longer flight,
Waves in its plumes the various light.

Such was that happy Garden-state,
While man there walked without a mate:
After a place so pure and sweet,
What other help could yet be meet!
But 'twas beyond a mortal's share
To wander solitary there:
Two paradises 'twere in one,
To live in Paradise alone.

How well the skilful gardener drew
Of flowers, and herbs, this dial new,
Where, from above, the milder sun
Does through a fragrant zodiac run,
And, as it works, the industrious bee
Computes its time as well as we!
How could such sweet and wholesome hours
Be reckoned, but with herbs and flowers?

¶ But there is no double meaning, no irony, in many good
poems. Here is Pope again.

From AN ESSAY ON MAN

Alexander Pope (1688–1744)

Know then thyself, presume not God to scan;
The proper study of mankind is man.
Placed on this isthmus of a middle state,
A being darkly wise, and rudely great:
With too much knowledge for the skeptic side,
With too much weakness for the stoic's pride,
He hangs between; in doubt to act, or rest;
In doubt to deem himself a god, or beast;
In doubt his mind or body to prefer;
Born but to die, and reasoning but to err;
Alike in ignorance, his reason such,
Whether he thinks too little, or too much:
Chaos of thought and passion, all confused;
Still by himself abused, or disabused;
Created half to rise, and half to fall;
Great Lord of all things, yet a prey to all;

Sole judge of truth, in endless error hurled:
The glory, jest, and riddle of the world!

¶ A contrast to both Pope and Marvell is Blake, whose "sick rose" is a symbol which does not bear any kind of translation. The word "sick" and the word "rose" appear immediately to contradict each other—and that is the point.

THE SICK ROSE

William Blake (*1757–1827*)

ᦂᦔ ᦺᦶ

O Rose, thou art sick!
The invisible worm,
That flies in the night,
In the howling storm,

Has found out thy bed
Of crimson joy,
And his dark secret love
Does thy life destroy.

¶ At other times Blake is not enigmatic at all in stating his beliefs. The next poem, which is sung as a hymn in many Protestant churches, refers to a belief that Jesus visited England during the unaccounted years of his life. The "dark Satanic Mills" are early factories.

---

[205]

"AND DID THOSE FEET IN ANCIENT TIME"

William Blake (1757–1827)

And did those feet in ancient time
　　Walk upon England's mountains green,
And was the holy Lamb of God
　　On England's pleasant pastures seen?

And did the Countenance Divine
　　Shine forth upon our clouded hills,
And was Jerusalem builded here
　　Among these dark Satanic Mills?

Bring me my bow of burning gold!
　　Bring me my arrows of desire!
Bring me my spear! O clouds, unfold!
　　Bring me my chariot of fire!

I will not cease from mental fight,
　　Nor shall my sword sleep in my hand,
Till we have built Jerusalem
　　In England's green and pleasant land.

"OUR BIRTH IS BUT A SLEEP . . ."

William Wordsworth (1770–1850)

Our birth is but a sleep and a forgetting:
The Soul that rises with us, our life's Star,
　Hath had elsewhere its setting,
　　And cometh from afar:

[206]

Not in entire forgetfulness,
    And not in utter nakedness,
But trailing clouds of glory do we come
    From God, who is our home:
Heaven lies about us in our infancy!
Shades of the prison-house begin to close
    Upon the growing Boy,
But he beholds the light, and whence it flows,
    He sees it in his joy;
The Youth, who daily farther from the east
    Must travel, still is Nature's Priest,
    And by the vision splendid
    Is on his way attended;
At length the Man perceives it die away,
And fade into the light of common day.

I AM

John Clare (1793–1864)

ੜ✷ ✷ੜ

I am: yet what I am none cares or knows,
    My friends forsake me like a memory lost;
I am the self-consumer of my woes,
    They rise and vanish in oblivious host,
Like shades in love and death's oblivion lost;
And yet I am, and live with shadows tost

Into the nothingness of scorn and noise,
    Into the living sea of waking dreams,
Where there is neither sense of life nor joys,
    But the vast shipwreck of my life's esteems;
And e'en the dearest—that I loved the best—
Are strange—nay rather stranger than the rest.

I long for scenes where man has never trod,
 A place where woman never smiled or wept;
There to abide with my Creator, God,
 And sleep as I in childhood sweetly slept:
Untroubling and untroubled where I lie,
The grass below—above the vaulted sky.

OZYMANDIAS

Percy Bysshe Shelley (1792–1822)

I met a traveler from an antique land
Who said: Two vast and trunkless legs of stone
Stand in the desert . . . Near them, on the sand,
Half sunk, a shattered visage lies, whose frown,
And wrinkled lip, and sneer of cold command,
Tell that its sculptor well those passions read
Which yet survive, stamped on these lifeless things,
The hand that mocked them, and the heart that fed:
And on the pedestal these words appear:
"My name is Ozymandias, king of kings:
Look on my works, ye Mighty, and despair!"
Nothing beside remains. Round the decay
Of that colossal wreck, boundless and bare
The lone and level sands stretch far away.

¶ Tradition has it that Landor wrote the next poem— really an epigram—when he was seventy years old. He was not really ready to depart for some time.

"I STROVE WITH NONE . . ."

Walter Savage Landor (1775–1864)

આ⊷ ⊷ઙ

I strove with none, for none was worth my strife:
    Nature I loved, and next to Nature, Art:
I warmed both hands before the fire of Life,
    It sinks; and I am ready to depart.

ALONE

Edgar Allan Poe (1809–1849)

આ⊷ ⊷ઙ

From childhood's hour I have not been
As others were; I have not seen
As others saw; I could not bring
My passions from a common spring.
From the same source I have not taken
My sorrow; I could not awaken
My heart to joy at the same tone;
And all I loved, I loved alone.
Then—in my childhood—in the dawn
Of a most stormy life was drawn
From every depth of good and ill
The mystery which binds me still:
From the torrent, or the fountain,
From the red cliff of the mountain,
From the sun that round me rolled
In its autumn tint of gold,
From the lightning in the sky
As it passed me flying by,
From the thunder and the storm,

And the cloud that took the form
(When the rest of Heaven was blue)
Of a demon in my view.

¶ One of the most popular poems of general advice is
Edward Fitzgerald's translation of *The Rubaiyat of Omar
Khayyam.*

From THE RUBAIYAT OF OMAR KHAYYAM OF NAISHAPUR

Edward Fitzgerald (1809–1883)

ෂ๑๏ ๏ෂ

Dreaming when Dawn's Left Hand was in the Sky
I heard a Voice within the Tavern cry,
    "Awake, my Little Ones, and fill the Cup
Before Life's Liquor in its Cup be dry."

And, as the Cock crew, those who stood before
The Tavern shouted—"Open then the Door!
    You know how little while we have to stay,
And, once departed, may return no more."

Come, fill the Cup, and in the Fire of Spring
The Winter Garment of Repentance fling:
    The Bird of Time has but a little way
To fly—and Lo! the Bird is on the Wing.

Here with a Loaf of Bread beneath the Bough,
A Flask of Wine, a Book of Verse—and Thou
    Beside me singing in the Wilderness—
And Wilderness is Paradise enow.

enow: enough

[210]

"How sweet is mortal Sovranty!"—think some:
Others—"How blest the Paradise to come!
 Ah, take the Cash in hand and waive the Rest;
Oh, the brave Music of a distant Drum!"

Look to the Rose that blows about us—"Lo,"
Laughing, she says, "into the World I blow:
 At once the silken Tassel of my Purse
Tear, and its Treasure on the Garden throw."

The worldly Hope men set their Hearts upon
Turns Ashes—or it prospers; and anon,
 Like Snow upon the Desert's dusty Face
Lighting a little Hour or two—is gone.

And those who husbanded the Golden Grain,
And those who flung it to the Winds like Rain,
 Alike to no such aureate Earth are turn'd
As, buried once, Men want dug up again.

Think, in this batter'd Caravanserai
Whose Doorways are alternate Night and Day,
 How Sultan after Sultan with his Pomp
Abode his Hour or two, and went his way.

They say the Lion and the Lizard keep
The Courts where Jamshyd gloried and drank deep;
 And Bahram, that great Hunter—the Wild Ass
Stamps o'er his Head, and he lies fast asleep.

I sometimes think that never blows so red
The Rose as where some buried Caesar bled;
 That every Hyacinth the Garden wears
Dropt in its Lap from some once lovely Head.

And this delightful Herb whose tender Green
Fledges the River's Lip on which we lean—
 Ah, lean upon it lightly! for who knows
From what once lovely Lip it springs unseen!

[211]

Ah, my Beloved, fill the Cup that clears
Today of past Regrets and future Fears—
    Tomorrow?—Why, Tomorrow I may be
Myself with Yesterday's Sev'n Thousand Years.

Lo! some we loved, the loveliest and best
That Time and Fate of all their Vintage prest,
    Have drunk their Cup a Round or two before,
And one by one crept silently to Rest.

And we, that now make merry in the Room
They left, and Summer dresses in new Bloom,
    Ourselves must we beneath the Couch of Earth
Descend, ourselves to make a Couch—for whom?

Ah, make the most of what we yet may spend,
Before we too into the Dust descend;
    Dust into Dust, and under Dust, to lie,
Sans Wine, sans Song, sans Singer, and—sans End!

Alike for those who for Today prepare,
And those that after a Tomorrow stare,
    A Muezzin from the Tower of Darkness cries
"Fools! your Reward is neither Here nor There!"

Why, all the Saints and Sages who discuss'd
Of the Two Worlds so learnedly, are thrust
    Like foolish Prophets forth; their Words to Scorn
Are scatter'd, and their Mouths are stopt with Dust.

Oh, come with old Khayyam, and leave the Wise
To talk; one thing is certain, that Life flies;
    One thing is certain, and the Rest is Lies;
The Flower that once has blown for ever dies.

Myself when young did eagerly frequent
Doctor and Saint, and heard great Argument
    About it and about: but evermore
Came out by the same Door as in I went.

With them the Seed of Wisdom did I sow,
And with my own hand labor'd it to grow:
    And this was all the Harvest that I reap'd—
"I came like Water, and like Wind I go."

Into this Universe, and *why* not knowing,
Nor *whence*, like Water willy-nilly flowing:
    And out of it, as Wind along the Waste,
I know not *whither*, willy-nilly blowing.

What, without asking, hither hurried *whence?*
And, without asking, *whither* hurried hence?
    Another and another Cup to drown
The memory of this Impertinence!

There was a Door to which I found no Key:
There was a Veil past which I could not see:
    Some little Talk awhile of Me and Thee
There seem'd—and then no more of Thee and Me.

Then to the rolling Heav'n itself I cried,
Asking, "What Lamp had Destiny to guide
    Her little Children stumbling in the Dark?"
And—"A blind Understanding!" Heav'n replied.

Then to this earthen Bowl did I adjourn
My Lip the secret Well of Life to learn:
    And Lip to Lip it murmur'd—"While you live
Drink!—for once dead you never shall return."

I think the Vessel, that with fugitive
Articulation answer'd, once did live,
    And merry-make; and the cold Lip I kiss'd
How many Kisses might it take—and give!

Ah, fill the Cup:—what boots it to repeat
How Time is slipping underneath our Feet:
    Unborn Tomorrow and dead Yesterday,
Why fret about them if Today be sweet!

One Moment in Annihilation's Waste,
One Moment, of the Well of Life to taste—
        The Stars are setting and the Caravan
Starts for the Dawn of Nothing—Oh, make haste!

How long, how long, in infinite Pursuit
Of This and That endeavor and dispute?
        Better be merry with the fruitful Grape
Than sadder after none, or bitter, Fruit.

You know, my Friends, how long since in my House
For a new Marriage I did make Carouse:
        Divorced old barren Reason from my Bed,
And took the Daughter of the Vine to Spouse.

The Grape that can with Logic absolute
The Two-and-Seventy jarring Sects confute:
        The subtle Alchemist that in a Trice
Life's leaden Metal into Gold transmute.

For in and out, above, about, below,
'T is nothing but a Magic Shadow-show,
        Play'd in a Box whose Candle is the Sun,
Round which we Phantom Figures come and go.

And if the Wine you drink, the Lip you press,
End in the Nothing all Things end in—Yes—
        Then fancy while Thou art, Thou art but what
Thou shalt be—Nothing—Thou shalt not be less.

The Moving Finger writes; and, having writ,
Moves on: nor all thy Piety nor Wit
        Shall lure it back to cancel half a Line,
Nor all thy Tears wash out a Word of it.

And that inverted Bowl we call The Sky,
Whereunder crawling coop't we live and die,
        Lift not thy hands to *It* for help—for It
Rolls impotently on as Thou or I.

Oh, Thou, who didst with Pitfall and with Gin
Beset the Road I was to wander in,
     Thou wilt not with Predestination round
Enmesh me, and impute my Fall to Sin?

Oh, Thou, who Man of baser Earth didst make,
And who with Eden didst devise the Snake;
     For all the Sin wherewith the Face of Man
Is blacken'd, Man's Forgiveness give—and take!

THE LAST WORD

Matthew Arnold (1822–1888)

Creep into thy narrow bed,
Creep, and let no more be said!
Vain thy onset! all stands fast;
Thou thyself must break at last.

Let the long contention cease!
Geese are swans, and swans are geese.
Let them have it how they will!
Thou art tired; best be still!

They out-talked thee, hiss'd thee; tore thee.
Better men fared thus before thee;
Fired their ringing shot and pass'd,
Hotly charged—and broke at last.

Charge once more, then, and be dumb!
Let the victors, when they come,
When the forts of folly fall,
Find thy body by the wall!

¶ Walt Whitman addresses his readers with an intimacy
few poets have ever attempted.

WHOEVER YOU ARE HOLDING
ME NOW IN HAND

Walt Whitman (1819–1892)

Whoever you are holding me now in hand,
Without one thing all will be useless,
I give you fair warning before you attempt me further,
I am not what you supposed, but far different.

Who is he that would become my follower?
Who would sign himself a candidate for my affections?
The way is suspicious, the result uncertain, perhaps destruc-
    tive,
You would have to give up all else, I alone would expect to
    be your sole and exclusive standard,
Your novitiate would even then be long and exhausting,
The whole past theory of your life and all conformity to the
    lives around you would have to be abandon'd,
Therefore release me now before troubling yourself any fur-
    ther, let go your hand from my shoulders,
Put me down and depart on your way.

Or else by stealth in some wood for trial,
Or back of a rock in the open air,
(For in any roof'd room of a house I emerge not, nor in
    company,
And in libraries I lie as one dumb, a gawk, or unborn, or
    dead),
But just possibly with you on a high hill, first watching lest
    any person for miles around approach unawares,
Or possibly with you sailing at sea, or on the beach of the sea
    or some quiet island,
Here to put your lips upon mine I permit you,
With the comrade's long-dwelling kiss or the new husband's
    kiss,
For I am the new husband and I am the comrade.

Or if you will, thrusting me beneath your clothing,
Where I may feel the throbs of your heart or rest upon your
    hip,
Carry me when you go forth over land or sea;
For thus merely touching you is enough, is best,
And thus touching you would I silently sleep and be carried
    eternally.

But these leaves conning you con at peril,
For these leaves and me you will not understand,
They will elude you at first and still more afterward, I will
    certainly elude you,
Even while you should think you had unquestionably caught
    me, behold!
Already you see I have escaped from you.

For it is not for what I have put into it that I have written this
    book,
Nor is it by reading it you will acquire it,
Nor do those know me best who admire me and vauntingly
    praise me,
Nor will the candidates for my love (unless at most a very
    few) prove victorious,
Nor will my poems do good only, they will do just as much
    evil, perhaps more,
For all is useless without that which you may guess at many
    times and not hit, that which I hinted at;
Therefore release me and depart on your way.

¶ The other side of Whitman's intimacy is the sense of
isolation which so many American poets have written
about.

THE MOST OF IT

Robert Frost (*1875–*)

He thought he kept the universe alone;
For all the voice in answer he could wake
Was but the mocking echo of his own
From some tree-hidden cliff across the lake.
Some morning from the boulder-broken beach
He would cry out on life, that what it wants
Is not its own love back in copy speech,
But counter-love, original response.
And nothing ever came of what he cried
Unless it was the embodiment that crashed
In the cliff's talus on the other side,
And then in the far distant water splashed,
But after a time allowed for it to swim,
Instead of proving human when it neared
And someone else additional to him,
As a great buck it powerfully appeared,
Pushing the crumpled water up ahead,
And landed pouring like a waterfall,
And stumbled through the rocks with horny tread,
And forced the underbrush—and that was all.

ACQUAINTED WITH THE NIGHT

Robert Frost (*1875–*)

I have been one acquainted with the night.
I have walked out in rain—and back in rain.
I have outwalked the furthest city light.

talus: rocky debris at foot of a cliff

I have looked down the saddest city lane.
I have passed by the watchman on his beat
And dropped my eyes, unwilling to explain.

I have stood still and stopped the sound of feet
When far away an interrupted cry
Came over houses from another street,

But not to call me back or say goodbye;
And further still at an unearthly height,
One luminary clock against the sky

Proclaimed the time was neither wrong nor right.
I have been one acquainted with the night.

SILENCE

Marianne Moore (*1887–*   )

꒰꒱

My father used to say,
"Superior people never make long visits,
have to be shown Longfellow's grave
or the glass flowers at Harvard.
Self-reliant like the cat—
that takes its prey to privacy,
the mouse's limp tail hanging like a shoelace from its mouth—
they sometimes enjoy solitude,
and can be robbed of speech
by speech which has delighted them.
The deepest feeling always shows itself in silence;
not in silence, but restraint."
Nor was he insincere in saying, "Make my house your inn."
Inns are not residences.

¶ Sixty years old and one of America's greatest poets, Ezra Pound was imprisoned at Pisa in 1945 by the American army. He had been convinced that America's entry into World War II was wrong, and had broadcast from Italy while the United States and Italy were at war. Caged in the open, under heavy wire, he wrote the *Pisan Cantos* which include the passage which follows:

"THE ANT'S A CENTAUR . . ."

Ezra Pound (1885–   )

The ant's a centaur in his dragon world.
Pull down thy vanity, it is not man
Made courage, or made order, or made grace,
  Pull down thy vanity, I say pull down.
Learn of the green world what can be thy place
In scaled invention or true artistry,
Pull down thy vanity,
      Paquin pull down!
The green casque has outdone your elegance.

"Master thyself, then others shall thee bear"
  Pull down thy vanity
Thou art a beaten dog beneath the hail,
A swollen magpie in a fitful sun,
Half black half white
Nor knowst'ou wing from tail
Pull down thy vanity
  How mean thy hates
Fostered in falsity,
  Pull down thy vanity,

Paquin: a dress designer

[220]

Rathe to destroy, niggard in charity,
Pull down thy vanity,
        I say pull down.
But to have done instead of not doing
        this is not vanity
To have, with decency, knocked
That a Blunt should open
        To have gathered from the air a live tradition
or from a fine old eye the unconquered flame
This is not vanity.
        Here error is all in the not done,
all in the diffidence that faltered.

SPRING AND ALL

William Carlos Williams (1883–)

§≈≈§

By the road to the contagious hospital
under the surge of the blue
mottled clouds driven from the
northeast—a cold wind. Beyond, the
waste of broad, muddy fields
brown with dried weeds, standing and fallen

patches of standing water
the scattering of tall trees

All along the road the reddish
purplish, forked, upstanding, twiggy
stuff of bushes and small trees
with dead, brown leaves under them
leafless vines—

Blunt: Wilfrid Scrawen Blunt, English poet.

Lifeless in appearance, sluggish
dazed spring approaches—

They enter the new world naked,
cold, uncertain of all
save that they enter. All about them
the cold, familar wind—

Now the grass, tomorrow
the stiff curl of wild carrot leaf
One by one objects are defined—
It quickens: clarity, outline of leaf

But now the stark dignity of
entrance—Still, the profound change
has come upon them: rooted they
grip down and begin to awaken.

I THINK CONTINUALLY OF THOSE

Stephen Spender (1909–   )

&ddd;

I think continually of those who were truly great.
Who, from the womb, remembered the soul's history
Through corridors of light where the hours are suns,
Endless and singing. Whose lovely ambition
Was that their lips, still touched with fire,
Should tell of the spirit clothed from head to foot in song.
And who hoarded from the Spring branches
The desires falling across their bodies like blossoms.

What is precious, is never to forget
The essential delight of the blood drawn from ageless springs
Breaking through rocks in worlds before our earth.

[222]

Never to deny its pleasure in the simple morning light
Nor its grave evening demand for love.
Never to allow gradually the traffic to smother
With noise and fog the flowering of the Spirit.

Near the snow, near the sun, in the highest fields
See how these names are fêted by the waving grass,
And by the streamers of white cloud
And whispers of wind in the listening sky;
The names of those who in their lives fought for life,
Who wore at their hearts the fire's center.
Born of the sun they traveled a short while towards the sun,
And left the vivid air signed with their honor.

MUSÉE DES BEAUX ARTS

W. H. Auden (1907–   )

About suffering they were never wrong,
The Old Masters: how well they understood
Its human position; how it takes place
While someone else is eating or opening a window or just
    walking dully along;
How, when the aged are reverently, passionately waiting
For the miraculous birth, there always must be
Children who did not specially want it to happen, skating
On a pond at the edge of the wood:
They never forgot
That even the dreadful martyrdom must run its course
Anyhow in a corner, some untidy spot
Where the dogs go on with their doggy life and the torturer's
    horse
Scratches its innocent behind on a tree.

[223]

In Brueghel's *Icarus*, for instance, how everything turns away
Quite leisurely from the disaster; the ploughman may
Have heard the splash, the forsaken cry,
But for him it was not an important failure; the sun shone
As it had to on the white legs disappearing into the green
Water; and the expensive delicate ship that must have seen
Something amazing, a boy falling out of the sky,
Had somewhere to get to and sailed calmly on.

A DREAM OF GOVERNORS

Louis Simpson (1923–   )

࿔ ࿔

The deepest dream is of mad governors.
                    —Mark Van Doren

The Knight from the world's end
Cut off the dragon's head.
The monster's only friend,
The Witch, insulting, fled.
The Knight was crowned, and took
His Lady. Good and gay,
They lived in a picture-book
Forever and a day.

Or else: When he had sat
So long, the King was old
And ludicrous and fat.
At feasts when poets told
How he had shed the blood
Of dragons long ago
He thought, Have I done good
To hear that I did so?

The chorus in a play
Declaimed: "The soul does well
Keeping the middle way."
He thought, That city fell;
Man's life is founded on
Folly at the extreme;
When all is said and done
The City is a dream.

At night the King alone
Went to the dragon's cave.
In moonlight on a stone
The Witch sat by the grave.
He grasped her by the hand
And said, "Grant what I ask.
Bring evil on the land
That I may have a task!"

The Queen has heard his tread;
She shuts the picture-book.
The King stands by the bed.
In silence as they look
Into each other's eyes
They see a buried thing
That creeps, begins to rise,
And spreads the dragon's wing.

DOLOR

Theodore Roethke (1908–   )

I have known the inexorable sadness of pencils,
Neat in their boxes, dolor of pad and paper-weight,
All the misery of manila folders and mucilage,
Desolation in immaculate public places,

Lonely reception room, lavatory, switchboard,
The unalterable pathos of basin and pitcher,
Ritual of multigraph, paper-clip, comma,
Endless duplication of lives and objects.
And I have seen dust from the walls of institutions,
Finer than flour, alive, more dangerous than silica,
Sift, almost invisible, through long afternoons of tedium,
Dripping a fine film on nails and delicate eyebrows,
Glazing the pale hair, the duplicate gray standard faces.

¶ Of course poets have often written on the subject of
poetry, too. Ben Jonson was such a figure to subsequent
poets that many of them were known as the "Sons of
Ben." Robert Herrick was an appreciative heir.

HIS PRAYER TO BEN JONSON

Robert Herrick (1591–1674)

ॐ ‿ ॐ

When I a verse shall make,
Know I have prayed thee,
For old religion's sake,
Saint Ben, to aid me.

Make the way smooth for me,
When I, thy Herrick,
Honoring thee, on my knee,
Offer my lyric.

Candles I'll give to thee,
And a new altar;
And thou, Saint Ben, shalt be
Writ in my psalter.

AN ODE FOR BEN JONSON

Robert Herrick (1591–1674)

Ah, Ben!
Say how or when
Shall we, thy guests,
Meet at those lyric feasts
Made at the Sun,
The Dog, the Triple Tun?
Where we such clusters had
As made us nobly wild, not mad;
And yet each verse of thine
Outdid the meat, outdid the frolic wine.

My Ben,
Or come again,
Or send to us
Thy wit's great overplus;
But teach us yet
Wisely to husband it,
Lest we that talent spend;
And having once brought to an end
That precious stock, the store
Of such a wit, the world should have no more.

¶ Keats's "Ode" is after all "On a Grecian Urn," and his subject is precisely the difference between his own, changing life and the static perfection of a work of art.

ODE ON A GRECIAN URN

John Keats (1795–1821)

Thou still unravished bride of quietness,
    Thou foster-child of silence and slow time,
Sylvan historian, who canst thus express
    A flowery tale more sweetly than our rhyme:
What leaf-fringed legend haunts about thy shape
    Of deities or mortals, or of both,
        In Tempe or the dales of Arcady?
    What men or gods are these? What maidens loath?
What mad pursuit? What struggle to escape?
    What pipes and timbrels? What wild ecstasy?

Heard melodies are sweet, but those unheard
    Are sweeter; therefore, ye soft pipes, play on;
Not to the sensual ear, but, more endear'd,
    Pipe to the spirit ditties of no tone:
Fair youth, beneath the trees, thou canst not leave
    Thy song, nor ever can those trees be bare;
        Bold Lover, never, never canst thou kiss,
    Though winning near the goal—yet, do not grieve;
She cannot fade, though thou hast not thy bliss,
    For ever wilt thou love, and she be fair!

And happy, happy boughs! that cannot shed
    Your leaves, nor ever bid the Spring adieu;
And, happy melodist, unwearied,
    For ever piping songs for ever new;
More happy love! more happy, happy love!
    For ever warm and still to be enjoy'd,
        For ever panting and for ever young;
All breathing human passion far above,
That leaves a heart high-sorrowful and cloy'd,
        A burning forehead, and a parching tongue.

Who are these coming to the sacrifice?
    To what green altar, O mysterious priest,
Lead'st thou that heifer lowing at the skies,
    And all her silken flanks with garlands drest?
What little town by river or sea shore,
    Or mountain-built with peaceful citadel,
    Is emptied of its folk, this pious morn?
    And, little town, thy streets for evermore
Will silent be; and not a soul to tell
    Why thou art desolate, can e'er return.

O Attic shape! Fair attitude! with brede
    Of marble men and maidens overwrought,
With forest branches and the trodden weed;
    Thou, silent form, dost tease us out of thought
As doth eternity: Cold Pastoral!
    When old age shall this generation waste,
    Thou shalt remain, in midst of other woe
    Than ours, a friend to man, to whom thou say'st,
"Beauty is truth, truth beauty,"—that is all
    Ye know on earth, and all ye need to know.

¶ Try reading the last line and a half this way: Keats is telling the urn that all *it* needs to know is that beauty is truth. By implication, Keats himself has to know that beauty and truth are different indeed. Beauty is perfect and changeless; his truth is the "other woe" of the last stanza.

MIND

Richard Wilbur (1921–)

Mind in its purest play is like some bat
That beats about in caverns all alone,
Contriving by a kind of senseless wit
Not to conclude against a wall of stone.

It has no need to falter or explore;
Darkly it knows what obstacles are there,
And so may weave and flitter, dip and soar
In perfect courses through the blackest air.

And has this simile a like perfection?
The mind is like a bat. Precisely. Save
That in the very happiest intellection
A graceful error may correct the cave.

IN MY CRAFT OR SULLEN ART

Dylan Thomas (1914–1953)

In my craft or sullen art
Exercised in the still night
When only the moon rages
And the lovers lie abed
With all their griefs in their arms,
I labor by singing light
Not for ambition or bread
Or the strut and trade of charms
On the ivory stages

[230]

But for the common wages
Of their most secret heart.
Not for the proud man apart
From the raging moon I write
On these spindrift pages
Nor for the towering dead
With their nightingales and psalms
But for the lovers, their arms
Round the griefs of the ages,
Who pay no praise or wages
Nor heed my craft or art.

FOR MY CONTEMPORARIES

J. V. Cunningham (1911–   )

How time reverses
The proud in heart!
I now make verses
Who aimed at art.

But I sleep well.
Ambitious boys
Whose big lines swell
With spiritual noise,

Despise me not!
And be not queasy
To praise somewhat:
Verse is not easy.

But rage who will.
Time that procured me
Good sense and skill
Of madness cured me.

[231]

POETRY

Marianne Moore (1887–   )

I, too, dislike it: there are things that are important beyond all
    this fiddle.
Reading it, however, with a perfect contempt for it, one dis-
    covers in
it after all, a place for the genuine.
    Hands that can grasp, eyes
    that can dilate, hair that can rise
      if it must, these things are important not because a
high-sounding interpretation can be put upon them but be-
    cause they are
useful. When they become so derivative as to become unin-
    telligible,
The same thing may be said for all of us, that we
    do not admire what
    we cannot understand: the bat
      holding on upside down or in quest of something to

eat, elephants pushing, a wild horse taking a roll, a tireless wolf
    under
a tree, the immovable critic twitching his skin like a horse that
    feels a flea, the base-
ball fan, the statistician—
    nor is it valid
    to discriminate against "business documents and

school-books"; all these phenomena are important. One must
    make a distinction
however: when dragged into prominence by half poets, the
    result is not poetry,
nor till the poets among us can be
    "literalists of
    the imagination"—above insolence and can present

for inspection, imaginary gardens with real toads in them, shall
        we have
it. In the meantime, if you demand on the one hand, the raw
        material of poetry in
    all its rawness and
    that which is on the other hand
        genuine, then you are interested in poetry.

¶ "I too, dislike it." What a strange beginning for a poem called "Poetry." Notice, however, that by the end of the poem Miss Moore has made a big claim for the art she dislikes but practices.

Wallace Stevens, people have said, is always writing about poetry. "Thirteen Ways of Looking at a Blackbird" may be about perception. But maybe it is more about how we can phrase, or formalize, our perceptions.

THIRTEEN WAYS OF LOOKING AT A BLACKBIRD

Wallace Stevens (*1879–1955*)

ৡ৺ ৶ঌ

I

Among twenty snowy mountains,
The only moving thing
Was the eye of the blackbird.

II

I was of three minds,
Like a tree
In which there are three blackbirds.

[233]

III

The blackbird whirled in the autumn winds.
It was a small part of the pantomime.

IV

A man and a woman
Are one.
A man and a woman and a blackbird
Are one.

V

I do not know which to prefer,
The beauty of inflections
Or the beauty of innuendoes,
The blackbird whistling
Or just after.

VI

Icicles filled the long window
With barbaric glass.
The shadow of the blackbird
Crossed it, to and fro.
The mood
Traced in the shadow
An indecipherable cause.

VII

O thin men of Haddam,
Why do you imagine golden birds?
Do you not see how the blackbird
Walks around the feet
Of the women about you?

VIII

I know noble accents
And lucid, inescapable rhythms;
But I know, too,
That the blackbird is involved
In what I know.

IX

When the blackbird flew out of sight,
It marked the edge
Of one of many circles.

X

At the sight of blackbirds
Flying in a green light,
Even the bawds of euphony
Would cry out sharply.

XI

He rode over Connecticut
In a glass coach.
Once, a fear pierced him,
In that he mistook
The shadow of his equipage
For blackbirds.

XII

The river is moving.
The blackbird must be flying.

XIII

It was evening all afternoon.
It was snowing

[235]

And it was going to snow.
The blackbird sat
In the cedar limbs.

¶ And this next one, if not about poetry, is at least about
the imagination.

DISILLUSIONMENT OF TEN O'CLOCK

Wallace Stevens (1879–1955)

The houses are haunted
By white night-gowns.
None are green,
Or purple with green rings,
Or green with yellow rings,
Or yellow with blue rings.
None of them are strange,
With socks of lace
And beaded ceintures.
People are not going
To dream of baboons and periwinkles.
Only, here and there, an old sailor,
Drunk and asleep in his boots,
Catches tigers
In red weather.

¶ There is a kind of poetry which is sometimes called pure.
Our pleasure resides in the sound of the words.

Chorus from ATALANTA IN CALYDON

Algernon Charles Swinburne (1837–1909)

When the hounds of spring are on winter's traces,
  The mother of months in meadow or plain
Fills the shadows and windy places
  With lisp of leaves and ripple of rain;
And the brown bright nightingale amorous
Is half assuaged for Itylus,
For the Thracian ships and the foreign faces,
  The tongueless vigil, and all the pain.

Come with bows bent and with emptying of quivers,
  Maiden most perfect, lady of light,
With a noise of winds and many rivers,
  With a clamor of waters, and with might;
Bind on thy sandals, O thou most fleet,
Over the splendor and speed of thy feet;
For the faint east quickens, the wan west shivers,
  Round the feet of the day and the feet of the night.

Where shall we find her, how shall we sing to her,
  Fold our hands round her knees, and cling?
O that man's heart were as fire and could spring to her,
  Fire, or the strength of the streams that spring!
For the stars and the winds are unto her
As raiment, as songs of the harp-player;
For the risen stars and the fallen cling to her,
  And the southwest-wind and the west-wind sing.

For winter's rains and ruins are over,
  And all the season of snows and sins;
The days dividing lover and lover,
  The light that loses, the night that wins;
And time remembered is grief forgotten,

And frosts are slain and flowers begotten,
And in green underwood and cover
    Blossom by blossom the spring begins.

The full streams feed on flower of rushes,
    Ripe grasses trammel a traveling foot,
The faint fresh flame of the young year flushes
    From leaf to flower and flower to fruit;
And fruit and leaf are as gold and fire,
And the oat is heard above the lyre,
And the hoofèd heel of a satyr crushes
    The chestnut-husk at the chestnut-root.

And Pan by noon and Bacchus by night,
    Fleeter of foot than the fleet-foot kid,
Follows with dancing and fills with delight
    The Maenad and the Bassarid;
And soft as lips that laugh and hide
The laughing leaves of the trees divide,
And screen from seeing and leave in sight
    The god pursuing, the maiden hid.

The ivy falls with the Bacchanal's hair
    Over her eyebrows hiding her eyes;
The wild vine slipping down leaves bare
    Her bright breast shortening into sighs;
The wild vine slips with the weight of its leaves,
But the berried ivy catches and cleaves
To the limbs that glitter, the feet that scare
    The wolf that follows, the fawn that flies.

¶ The sound calls attention to itself more than the meaning does. Nonsense verse is another pleasure which is at least independent of thinking.

THE OWL AND THE PUSSY-CAT

Edward Lear (1812–1888)

The Owl and the Pussy-cat went to sea
    In a beautiful pea-green boat:
They took some honey, and plenty of money
    Wrapped up in a five-pound note.
The Owl looked up to the stars above,
    And sang to a small guitar,
"O lovely Pussy, O Pussy, my love,
    What a beautiful Pussy you are,
        You are,
        You are!
    What a beautiful Pussy you are!"

Pussy said to the Owl, "You elegant fowl,
    How charmingly sweet you sing!
Oh! let us be married; too long we have tarried:
    But what shall we do for a ring?"
They sailed away, for a year and a day,
    To the land where the bong-tree grows;
And there in a wood a Piggy-wig stood,
    With a ring at the end of his nose,
        His nose,
        His nose,
    With a ring at the end of his nose.

"Dear Pig, are you willing to sell for one shilling
    Your ring?" Said the Piggy, "I will."
So they took it away, and were married next day
    By the turkey who lives on the hill.
They dined on mince and slices of quince,
    Which they ate with a runcible spoon;
And hand in hand, on the edge of the sand,

They danced by the light of the moon,
      The moon,
      The moon,
They danced by the light of the moon.

BY WAY OF PREFACE

Edward Lear (1812–1888)

How pleasant to know Mr. Lear!
      Who has written such volumes of stuff!
Some think him ill-tempered and queer,
      But a few think him pleasant enough.

His mind is concrete and fastidious,
      His nose is remarkably big;
His visage is more or less hideous,
      His beard it resembles a wig.

He has ears, and two eyes, and ten fingers,
      Leastways if you reckon two thumbs;
Long ago he was one of the singers,
      But now he is one of the dumbs.

He sits in a beautiful parlor,
      With hundreds of books on the wall;
He drinks a great deal of Marsala,
      But never gets tipsy at all.

He has many friends, laymen and clerical,
      Old Foss is the name of his cat:
His body is perfectly spherical,
      He weareth a runcible hat.

When he walks in a waterproof white,
    The children run after him so!
Calling out, "He's come out in his night-
    Gown, that crazy old Englishman, oh!"

He weeps by the side of the ocean,
    He weeps on the top of the hill;
He purchases pancakes and lotion,
    And chocolate shrimps from the mill.

He reads but he cannot speak Spanish,
    He cannot abide ginger-beer:
Ere the days of his pilgrimage vanish,
    How pleasant to know Mr. Lear!

"anyone lived in a pretty how town"

E. E. Cummings (1894–1962)

❧

anyone lived in a pretty how town
(with up so floating many bells down)
spring summer autumn winter
he sang his didn't he danced his did.

Women and men(both little and small)
cared for anyone not at all
they sowed their isn't they reaped their same
sun moon stars rain

children guessed(but only a few
and down they forgot as up they grew
autumn winter spring summer)
that noone loved him more by more

[241]

when by now and tree by leaf
she laughed his joy she cried his grief
bird by snow and stir by still
anyone's any was all to her

someones married their everyones
laughed their cryings and did their dance
(sleep wake hope and then)they
said their nevers they slept their dream

stars rain sun moon
(and only the snow can begin to explain
how children are apt to forget to remember
with up so floating many bells down)

one day anyone died I guess
(and noone stooped to kiss his face)
busy folk buried them side by side
little by little and was by was

all by all and deep by deep
and more by more they dream their sleep
noone and anyone earth by april
wish by spirit and if by yes.

Women and men(both dong and ding)
summer autumn winter spring
reaped their sowing and went their came
sun moon stars rain

¶ The same poet can leave nonsense far behind. E. E. Cummings is best when he is satirical. At the end of his poem, Cummings can use a phrase which is *like* nonsense but which makes sense as a symbol of the outraged imagination.

"the Cambridge ladies who live in furnished souls"

E. E. Cummings (1894–1962)

ช๛ ๏ร

the Cambridge ladies who live in furnished souls
are unbeautiful and have comfortable minds
(also, with the church's protestant blessings
daughters, unscented shapeless spirited)
they believe in Christ and Longfellow, both dead,
are invariably interested in so many things—
at the present writing one still finds
delighted fingers knitting for the is it Poles?
perhaps. While permanent faces coyly bandy
scandal of Mrs. N and Professor D
. . . the Cambridge ladies do not care, above
Cambridge if sometimes in its box of
sky lavender and cornerless, the
moon rattles like a fragment of angry candy

THE LEGS

Robert Graves (1885–)

ช๛ ๏ร

There was this road,
And it led up-hill,
And it led down-hill,
And round and in and out.

And the traffic was legs,
Legs from the knees down,
Coming and going,
Never pausing.

[243]

And the gutters gurgled
With the rain's overflow,
And the sticks on the pavement
Blindly tapped and tapped.

What drew the legs along
Was the never-stopping,
And the senseless, frightening
Fate of being legs.

Legs for the road,
The road for legs,
Resolutely nowhere
In both directions.

My legs at least
Were not in that rout:
On grass by the road-side
Entire I stood,

Watching the unstoppable
Legs go by
With never a stumble
Between step and step.

Though my smile was broad
The legs could not see,
Though my laugh was loud
The legs could not hear.

My head dizzied, then:
I wondered suddenly,
Might I too be a walker
From the knees down?

Gently I touched my shins.
The doubt unchained them:
They had run in twenty puddles
Before I regained them.

[244]

BAGPIPE MUSIC

Louis MacNeice (1907–)

It's no go the merrygoround, it's no go the rickshaw,
All we want is a limousine and a ticket for the peepshow.
Their knickers are made of crêpe-de-chine, their shoes are
      made of python,
Their halls are lined with tiger rugs and their walls with heads
      of bison.

John MacDonald found a corpse, put it under the sofa,
Waited till it came to life and hit it with a poker,
Sold its eyes for souvenirs, sold its blood for whiskey,
Kept its bones for dumb-bells to use when he was fifty.

It's no go the Yogi-Man, it's no go Blavatsky,
All we want is a bank balance and a bit of skirt in a taxi.

Annie MacDougall went to milk, caught her foot in the
      heather,
Woke to hear a dance record playing of Old Vienna.
It's no go your maidenheads, it's no go your culture,
All we want is a Dunlop tyre and the devil mend the puncture.

The Laird o'Phelps spent Hogmannay declaring he was sober;
Counted his feet to prove the fact and found he had one foot
      over.
Mrs. Carmichael had her fifth, looked at the job with repul-
      sion,
Said to the midwife "Take it away; I'm through with over-
      production."

It's no go the gossip column, it's no go the Ceilidh,

Blavatsky: Madame Blavatsky, a spiritualist
Hogmannay: Scottish celebration at New Year's. *Ceilidh:* gossip

[245]

All we want is a mother's help and a sugar-stick for the baby.

Willie Murray cut his thumb, couldn't count the damage,
Took the hide of an Ayrshire cow and used it for a bandage.
His brother caught three hundred cran when the seas were lavish,
Threw the bleeders back in the sea and went upon the parish.

It's no go the Herring Board, it's no go the Bible,
All we want is a packet of fags when our hands are idle.
It's no go the picture palace, it's no go the stadium,
It's no go the country cot with a pot of pink geraniums.
It's no go the Government grants, it's no go the elections,
Sit on your arse for fifty years and hang your hat on a pension.

It's no go my honey love, it's no go my poppet;
Work your hands from day to day, the winds will blow the profit.
The glass is falling hour by hour, the glass will fall for ever,
But if you break the bloody glass you won't hold up the weather.

¶ Louis MacNeice wrote "Bagpipe Music" during the great depression of the thirties, and of course the background is English. Kenneth Fearing wrote during the same economic disaster in America, using sarcastic parodies of advertising to make his point about the insignificance of the individual in a mass society.

---

glass: barometer

DIRGE

Kenneth Fearing (1902–1960)

ξ∂∞ ∞δξ

1-2-3 was the number he played but today the number came
    3-2-1;
    bought his Carbine at 30 and it went to 29; had the favor-
    ite at Bowie but the track was slow—

O, executive type, would you like to drive a floating power,
    knee-action, silk-upholstered six? Wed a Hollywood
    star? Shoot the course in 58? Draw the ace, king, jack?
    O, fellow with a will who won't take no, watch out for
    three cigarettes on the same, single match; O, demo-
    cratic voter born in August under Mars, beware of liq-
    uidated rails—

Denouement to denouement, he took a personal pride in the
    certain, certain way he lived his own, private life,
    but nevertheless, they shut off his gas; nevertheless, the
    bank foreclosed; nevertheless, the landlord called; nev-
    ertheless, the radio broke,

And twelve o'clock arrived just once too often,
    Just the same he wore one gray tweed suit, bought one
    straw hat, drank one straight Scotch, walked one short
    step, took one long look, drew one deep breath,
    just one too many,

And wow he died as wow he lived,
    going whop to the office and blooie home to sleep and
    biff got married and bam had children and oof got
    fired,
    zowie did he live and zowie did he die,

With who the hell are you at the corner of his casket, and
    where the hell we going on the right hand silver knob,

and who the hell cares walking second from the end
with an American Beauty wreath from why the hell
not,

Very much missed by the circulation staff of the New York
Evening Post; deeply, deeply mourned by the B.M.T.,

Wham, Mr. Roosevelt; pow, Sears Roebuck; awk, big dipper;
bop, summer rain;
bong, Mr., bong, Mr., bong, Mr., bong.

¶ There were poems by W. B. Yeats on pages 179–182.
Here is a nonsensical poem he wrote when he was an old
man, later than all the other poems.

THE PILGRIM

William Butler Yeats (1865–1939)

I fasted for some forty days on bread and buttermilk,
For passing round the bottle with girls in rags or silk,
In country shawl or Paris cloak, had put my wits astray,
And what's the good of women, for all that they can say
Is fol de rol de rolly O.

Round Lough Derg's holy island I went upon the stones,
I prayed at all the Stations upon my marrow-bones,
And there I found an old man, and though I prayed all day
And that old man beside me, nothing would he say
But fol de rol de rolly O.

[248]

All know that all the dead in the world about that place are
  stuck,
And that should mother seek her son she'd have but little luck
Because the fires of Purgatory have ate their shapes away;
I swear to God I questioned them, and all they had to say
Was fol de rol de rolly O.

A great black ragged bird appeared when I was in the boat;
Some twenty feet from tip to tip had it stretched rightly out,
With flopping and with flapping it made a great display,
But I never stopped to question, what could the boatman say
But fol de rol de rolly O.

Now I am in the public-house and lean upon the wall,
So come in rags or come in silk, in cloak or country shawl,
And come with learned lovers or with what men you may,
For I can put the whole lot down, and all I have to say
Is fol de rol de rolly O.

¶ Poems can be solid political satire, too, like Rochester's
epitaph on Charles II on page 59, or like this poem by
Byron.

"WHEN A MAN HATH NO FREEDOM TO FIGHT FOR AT HOME"

George Gordon, Lord Byron (1788–1824)

❧ ⋄ ☙

When a man hath no freedom to fight for at home,
  Let him combat for that of his neighbors;
Let him think of the glories of Greece and of Rome,
  And get knocked on the head for his labors.

To do good to Mankind is the chivalrous plan,
    And is always as nobly requited;
Then battle for Freedom wherever you can,
    And, if not shot or hanged, you'll get knighted.

¶ And there are all sorts of possibilities for levity. The drinking song is a traditional sort.

DRINKING

Abraham Cowley (1618–1667)

ફ⟩◦⟨ફ

The thirsty earth soaks up the rain,
And drinks and gapes for drink again;
The plants suck in the earth, and are
With constant drinking fresh and fair;
The sea itself (which one would think
Should have but little need of drink)
Drinks twice ten thousand rivers up,
So filled that they o'erflow the cup.
The busy sun (and one would guess
By's drunken fiery face no less)
Drinks up the sea, and when he's done,
The moon and stars drink up the sun:
They drink and dance by their own light,
They drink and revel all the night.
Nothing in nature's sober found,
But an eternal health goes round.
Fill up the bowl, then, fill it high!
Fill all the glasses there—for why
Should every creature drink but I?
Why, man of morals, tell me why?

[250]

¶ We have reached the outer limits of levity in the last few poems. There is no reason why poems should not make us laugh, and most of our greatest poets have shown us their lighter side.

Yet to conclude an introductory anthology of poetry with a group of comic poems would be misleading. A better ending could be provided by one poet who contains in his own works stories, characters, elegies, love poems, philosophy and humor. The universal genius of English poetry is William Shakespeare.

He writes great songs:

"FEAR NO MORE . . ."

William Shakespeare (1564–1616)

Fear no more the heat o' the sun,
    Nor the furious winter's rages.
Thou thy worldly task hast done,
    Home art gone, and ta'en thy wages.
Golden lads and girls all must,
As chimney-sweepers, come to dust.

Fear no more the frown o' the great.
    Thou art past the tyrant's stroke;
Care no more to clothe and eat.
    To thee the reed is as the oak.
The sceptre, learning, physic, must
All follow this and come to dust.

Fear no more the lightning-flash,
    Nor the all-dreaded thunder-stone.

Fear not slander, censure rash.
Thou hast finished joy and moan.
All lovers young, all lovers must
Consign to thee and come to dust.

"WHEN ICICLES HANG BY THE WALL"

ॐ ॐ

When icicles hang by the wall,
And Dick the shepherd blows his nail,
And Tom bears logs into the hall,
And milk comes frozen home in pail,
When blood is nipt, and ways be foul,
Then nightly sings the staring owl—
To-whit to-who.
        A merry note,
        While greasy Joan doth keel the pot.

When all aloud the wind doth blow,
And coughing drowns the Parson's saw,
And birds sit brooding in the snow,
And Marian's nose looks red and raw,
When roasted crabs hiss in the bowl,
Then nightly sings the staring owl—
Tu-whit to-who.
        A merry note,
        While greasy Joan doth keel the pot.

¶ And sonnets:

---

keel: cool   *crabs:* crab-apples

Let me not to the marriage of true minds
Admit impediments. Love is not love
Which alters when it alteration finds,
Or bends with the remover to remove.
O no! it is an ever-fixèd mark
That looks on tempests and is never shaken;
It is the star to every wandering bark,
Whose worth's unknown, although his height be taken.
Love's not Time's fool, though rosy lips and cheeks
Within his bending sickle's compass come;
Love alters not with his brief hours and weeks,
But bears it out even to the edge of doom.
    If this be error and upon me proved,
    I never writ, nor no man ever loved.

That time of year thou mayst in me behold
When yellow leaves, or none, or few, do hang
Upon those boughs which shake against the cold,
Bare ruined choirs, where late the sweet birds sang.
In me thou see'st the twilight of such day
As after sunset fadeth in the west,
Which by and by black night doth take away,
Death's second self, that seals up all in rest.
In me thou see'st the glowing of such fire,
That on the ashes of his youth doth lie
As the death-bed whereon it must expire,
Consumed with that which it was nourished by.
    This thou perceivest, which makes thy love more strong,
    To love that well which thou must leave ere long.

Shall I compare thee to a summer's day?
Thou art more lovely and more temperate:
Rough winds do shake the darling buds of May,
And summer's lease hath all too short a date.
Sometime too hot the eye of heaven shines,
And often is his gold complexion dimmed.
And every fair from fair sometimes declines,

By chance or nature's changing course untrimmed.
But thy eternal summer shall not fade,
Nor lose possession of that fair thou owest,
Nor shall Death brag thou wanderest in his shade
When in eternal lines to time thou growest.
>   So long as men can breathe or eyes can see,
>   So long lives this and this gives life to thee.

They that have power to hurt, and will do none,
That do not do the thing, they most do show,
Who moving others, are themselves as stone,
Unmoved, cold, and to temptation slow:
They rightly do inherit heaven's graces
And husband nature's riches from expense.
They are the lords and owners of their faces,
Others but stewards of their excellence.
The summer's flower is to the summer sweet,
Though to itself it only live and die,
But if that flower with base infection meet,
The basest weed outbraves his dignity.
>   For sweetest things turn sourest by their deeds.
>   Lilies that fester smell far worse than weeds.

When in disgrace with Fortune and men's eyes
I all alone beweep my outcast state,
And trouble deaf heaven with my bootless cries,
And look upon my self and curse my fate.
Wishing me like to one more rich in hope,
Featur'd like him, like him with friends possest,
Desiring this man's art, and that man's scope,
With what I most enjoy contented least,
Yet in these thoughts my self almost despising,
Haply I think on thee, and then my state,
(Like to the Lark at break of day arising)
From sullen earth sings hymns at Heaven's gate,
>   For thy sweet love remembered such wealth brings,
>   That then I scorn to change my state with kings.

Not marble, nor the gilded monuments
Of princes, shall outlive this powerful rhyme.
But you shall shine more bright in these contents
Than unswept stone, besmeared with sluttish time.
When wasteful war shall statues overturn,
And broils root out the work of masonry,
Nor Mars his sword nor war's quick fire shall burn
The living record of your memory.
'Gainst death and all-oblivious enmity.
Shall you pace forth—your praise shall still find room
Even in the eyes of all posterity
That wear this world out to the ending doom.
    So, till the judgment that yourself arise,
    You live in this, and dwell in lovers' eyes.

¶ And he is greatest as a playwright:

From "KING HENRY THE FIFTH"

કે~ ৬১

Once more unto the breach, dear friends, once more;
Or close the wall up with our English dead!
In peace there's nothing so becomes a man
As modest stillness and humility.
But when the blast of war blows in our ears,
Then imitate the action of the tiger,
Stiffen the sinews, summon up the blood,
Disguise fair nature with hard-favored rage.
Then lend the eye a terrible aspect,
Let it pry through the portage of the head
Like the brass cannon. Let the brow o'erwhelm it
As fearfully as doth a gallèd rock
O'erhand and jutty his confounded base,

[255]

Swilled with the wild and wasteful ocean.
Now set the teeth and stretch the nostril wide,
Hold hard the breath, and bend up every spirit
To his full height. On, on, you noble English,
Whose blood is fet from fathers of war proof!
Fathers that, like so many Alexanders,
Have in these parts from morn till even fought,
And sheathed their swords for lack of argument.
Dishonor not your mothers. Now attest
That those whom you called fathers did beget you.
Be copy now to men of grosser blood,
And teach them how to war. And you, good yeomen,
Whose limbs were made in England, show us here
The mettle of your pasture. Let us swear
That you are worth your breeding which I doubt not,
For there is none of you so mean and base
That hath not noble lustre in your eyes.
I see you stand like greyhounds in the slips,
Straining upon the start. The game's afoot.
Follow your spirit, and upon this charge
Cry "God for Harry, England, and Saint George!"

From "HAMLET"

ح‍و‍ ع‍ق

To be, or not to be: that is the question.
Whether 'tis nobler in the mind to suffer
The slings and arrows of outrageous fortune,
Or to take arms against a sea of troubles
And by opposing end them. To die to sleep—
No more, and, by a sleep to say we end
The heartache and the thousand natural shocks
That flesh is heir to. 'Tis a consummation
Devoutly to be wished. To die, to sleep;

fet: fetched

[256]

To sleep—perchance to dream. Ay, there's the rub,
For in that sleep of death what dreams may come
When we have shuffled off this mortal coil,
Must give us pause. There's the respect
That makes calamity of so long life.
For who would bear the whips and scorns of time,
The oppressor's wrong, the proud man's contumely
The pangs of despised love, law's delay,
The insolence of office, and the spurns
That patient merit of the unworthy takes,
When he himself might his quietus make
With a bare bodkin? Who would fardels bear,
To grunt and sweat under a weary life,
But that the dread of something after death,
The undiscover'd country from whose bourn
No traveler returns, puzzles the will,
And makes us rather bear those ills we have
Than fly to others that we know not of?
Thus conscience does make cowards of us all,
And thus the native hue of resolution
Is sicklied o'er with the pale cast of thought,
And enterprises of great pitch and moment
With this regard their currents turn awry,
And lose the name of action.

From "AS YOU LIKE IT"

ॐ ॐ

All the world's a stage,
And all the men and women merely players.
They have their exits and their entrances,
And one man in his time plays many parts,
His acts being seven ages. At first the infant,
Mewling and puking in the nurse's arms.

respect: reason   *fardels:* burdens

[257]

And then the whining schoolboy, with his satchel,
And shining morning face, creeping like snail
Unwillingly to school. And then the lover,
Sighing like furnace, with a woeful ballad
Made to his mistress' eyebrow. Then a soldier,
Full of strange oaths, and bearded like the pard,
Jealous in honor, sudden and quick in quarrel,
Seeking the bubble reputation
Even in the cannon's mouth. And then the justice,
In fair round belly with good capon lined,
With eyes severe, and beard of formal cut,
Full of wise saws and modern instances,
And so he plays his part. The sixth age shifts
Into the lean and slippered pantaloon,
With spectacles on nose and pouch on side,
His youthful hose well saved, a world too wide
For his shrunk shank, and his big manly voice,
Turning again toward childish treble, pipes
And whistles in his sound. Last scene of all,
That ends this strange eventful history,
Is second childishness and more oblivion
Sans teeth, sans eyes, sans taste, sans everything.

INDEX OF AUTHORS

INDEX OF TITLES